4,000 Years
In Thirteen Weeks

by Sue Crabtree

Published by
21st Century Christian
2809 Granny White Pike • Nashville, TN 37204

Contents

Preface

Many Christians do not know the history of the Old Testament and how it all fits together. Often when we study an Old Testament survey, we spend so much time going through the Old Testament that we lose the big picture. It was my desire to write a book that gives facts to aid in study, questions to make one think, and challenges to involve Christians in the learning process. I hope this book will be used both in Bible classes and in homes as a study guide for the Old Testament. A Bible dictionary will be useful for verification of events and characters.

This study can be completed either in thirteen weeks or it may be extended to one year by spending four weeks on each lesson. Each student and teacher can make adjustments to fit the situation.

I am indebted to many great teachers who led me in this study. Many of the ideas presented here were gleaned from others.

May we have a strong desire to grasp knowledge, attitudes and skills from these Old Testament stories.

Sue Crabtree

Format of the Lessons

Fact Sheets: The fact sheets include outlines of the materials, character lists and maps.

Help Sheets: Extra study materials are provided.

Map Searches: Challenges are given to use maps for locating places under study. Maps are provided.

Questions: Short answer and thought questions are provided for the student.

Application: An application lesson is given with questions for further thought and study.

Special Challenge: Each section has several special challenges. Each person can choose challenges on the list that best meet needs and desires.

Suggestions for Teaching   Several suggestions are made about how to conduct the class effectively. Teaching options are given along with a sharing suggestion. This author feels that a sharing period is important because it involves every student in the learning and sets a positive atmosphere in a classroom. Sharing usually has to be limited to classes of 30 or fewer because of the time element.

Answers: Answers to the short answer questions are in the back of the book.

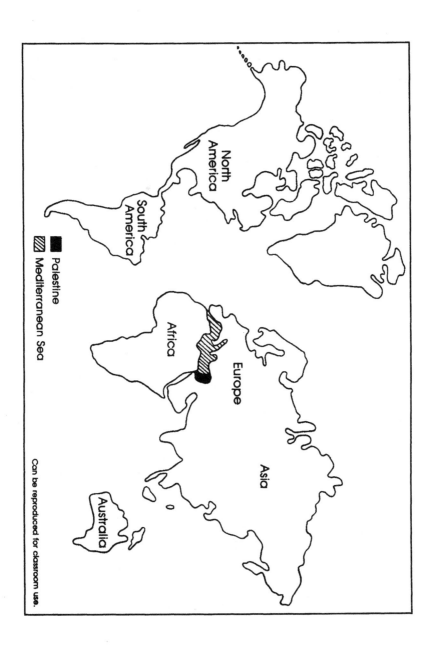

North America

South America

■ Palestine

▨ Mediterranean Sea

Africa

Europe

Asia

Australia

Can be reproduced for classroom use.

9

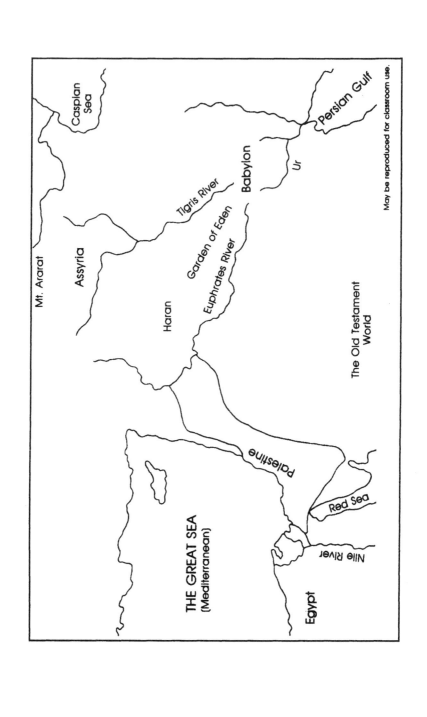

Mt. Ararat

Caspian
Sea

Assyria

Tigris River

Haran

Garden of Eden

Babylon

Euphrates River

Ur

Persian Gulf

The Old Testament
World

Palestine

Red Sea

THE GREAT SEA
(Mediterranean)

Nile River

Egypt

Chapter One

Genesis

GENESIS—A BOOK OF BEGINNING

The study of Genesis is a fascinating story of people, places, moves, commitment and unfaithfulness. The book begins with God creating the world and it tells the stories of the great flood and of Abraham's family and travels. It covers 2,500 years of Bible history and reads like a storybook with the touch of God's hand in it all.

FACT SHEET ON GENESIS

Genesis: means beginning
written by Moses
covers 2,500 years of history
has 50 chapters
begins with creation
ends with children of Israel living in Egypt
and all is well with them

BRIEF OUTLINE

Chapter/s	Event or Person/s
1, 2	Creation
3	Fall of Man
4	Cain and Abel
5	Generations (Adam-Noah)
6-9	Noah
10	Generations of Noah
11	Tower of Babel & Generations (Noah-Abraham)
12-25	Abraham
25-28	Isaac
29-36	Jacob
37-50	Joseph

MAP SEARCH

Garden of Eden (Mesopotamia Valley)
Mt. Ararat (where the ark rested)
Ur of Chaldees (Abraham's first home)
Haran (Terah dies, Abraham leaves his brother Nahor there)
Canaan (the promised land)
Egypt (Joseph is sold as a slave, Jacob's family moves there)
Hebron (Cave of Macpelah—burial ground for Abraham and his
   family) See map on page 46.
Bethel (Promises made to Jacob)
Bethlehem (Rachel's burial place)

* See maps on pages 10 and 46.

SOME CHARACTERISTICS OF THE PATRIARCHAL AGE

1. **Nomadic:**
    Founders, not of cities, but of race and a faith; wanderers with a purpose.
2. **Patriarchal Father:**
    (1)   Ruler of family   (3)   Family Priest
    (2)   Military Chieftain   (4)   Family Prophet
3. **Conceptions about God:**
    (1)   Unity   (3)   Universality of God
    (2)   No nature worship   (4)   Holiness of God
4. **Forms of Worship:**
    No temple, feasts or sabbath. There were altars, animal sacrifices, vows, prayers, tithes and circumcision.
5. **Degree of Civilization:**
    Nomads, but not barbarians; in contrast with Chaldeans and Egyptians. Shepherds and practical agriculture. Had money and jewelry.
6. **Significance of the Covenant:**
    Made to Abraham, Isaac and Jacob: land, nation and seed of Christ.
7. **Family:**
    Polygamy. (However, love shown between Abraham and Sarah and Isaac and Rebekah.) Woman's position was not degrading. Punishment for adultery. Slavery treated with respect, religious privileges.
8. **Religion:**
    Believed in a god above and beyond nature, personal omnipotent, holy God. Revealed Himself by angelic appearances, dreams, visions. Could console, rebuke, punish, strengthen. Think of Abraham's interceding on behalf of Sodom and Gomorrah, Jacob's wrestling with an angel, Joseph's believing.
9. **Character of the Patriarch:**
    Never represented as perfect, faults are exposed, no ideal history.

SHORT ANSWER QUESTIONS ON GENESIS

1. Genesis means _____.

2. Genesis covers _____ years.

3. Genesis has _____ chapters.

4. The author of Genesis is _____.

5. Genesis begins with _____.

6. Genesis ends with the children of Israel _____
   _____.

7. The main characters in Genesis are _____,
   _____, _____, _____,
   _____, and _____.

8. Who built the ark? _____

9. Sons of Noah? _____, _____,
   _____

10. Father of the faithful? _____

11. Isaac's wife? _____

12. Esau's brother? _____

13. Mother of Joseph? _____

14. Abraham's first two sons? _____ and _____

15. Abraham's father? _____

THOUGHT QUESTIONS

1. Give a lesson that we can learn from each: Eve, Sarah, Hagar and Lot's wife.

2. How do we see the providence of God in the book of Genesis (especially in the life of Joseph)?

SPECIAL CHALLENGES IN GENESIS

For volunteers only. Choose one or more you would like to do this week.

1. Memorize the outline of Genesis.
2. Memorize the first 10 generations found in Genesis 5.
3. Memorize what God created on each day of creation. (Genesis 1)
4. Read the book of Genesis this week.
5. Make a list of lessons you can learn from Genesis.
6. Be able to identify all the characters on the character list.
7. Make a collage or picture representing the book of Genesis.
8. Write a song or a poem about one of the stories in Genesis. Put the words to a familiar tune, like "Three Blind Mice."

APPLICATION: Genesis 24

Tell the story of the servant choosing a wife for Isaac. The servant was looking for a woman who would offer him and his camels a drink. The servant of Abraham had ten camels in his caravan and each camel could drink as much as thirty gallons of water. This meant that Rebekah could have drawn as many as 300 gallons of water. Was the servant looking for a woman who would go the second mile?

What are some examples of second mile service that we can put in our lives?

Give an example of a time when you went the second mile and you reaped rewards. Read Matthew 5:47 and make application to your life.

What can you do this week to be like Rebekah?

SUGGESTIONS FOR TEACHING

Sharing: Have each class member share with the group. Always give them an option of passing if they don't want to share. (Let them say, "I'm just glad to be here" if they don't want to share. This always gets a laugh and makes everyone feel comfortable.)

Abraham and Sarah moved from their home in Ur to a new land that God gave them. Tell about a time when you moved and the problems you encountered in the move. (Encourage members to be brief.)

Prayer: Take prayer requests and encourage members to give spiritual requests as well as physical. Also, remember thanksgiving.

Options: (Depends upon maturity, Bible knowledge, time and class arrangement.)

1. Review fact sheets, answer questions, find places on the map and talk about application.

2. Teacher, or a student, reviews the history in Genesis using a map to move from Adam to Noah to Abraham to Abraham's family. On the map, show the promised land and the move to Egypt which we read about in the end of the book. Let students take notes and write a summary.

3. Have students report on some of the characters making application to lives today.

4. Encourage those who volunteer to do the challenges and share these with the class.

5. Encourage the reading of the book of Genesis outside class and the sharing of thoughts with the class.

6. Make a set of character cards or flash cards to use in drill with the class. Write each column of words in a different color. Learn all the first color before proceeding to the second. Work with the color of the third column only after the class has mastered the first two.

7. Make transparencies of the maps and use them throughout this study.

Remember, the more participation, the more learning.

Genesis

God created Adam
In His image He said.
And then added Eve
And to Eden they head.

Life was tranquil and peaceful and full of the best,
But Eve wanted more and failed the first test.
The serpent was wily—yes, sly like a fox.
Better she had greeted him with a handful of rocks.

But to make matters worse, as so many of us do,
She didn't stop at disobeying; she caused Adam to sin, too.
And because she ate from the tree which was forbidden,
She suddenly felt strongly her body should be hidden.

Leaves were the fabric of choice because cloth was yet to be
made.
But the price of her sin was just beginning to be paid.
The couple was cast out from Eden, their home,
and to keep alive they were forced to labor and roam.

Now hunger and sickness and strife was their lot,
and the experience of childbirth was added to the knowledge
Eve got.
There are lessons a plenty we can learn from this now—
Obey, don't be greedy and take seriously the vow
Of living a life with God as your guide
And be thankful a heap for the grace He provides.

—Faye Gibson

A Genesis Rap

One, two the world began,
Chapter three: The fall of man.

Chapter four: Abel's no more.

Chapter five: There's a revelation
From Adam to Noah is ten generations.

Six, seven, eight and nine,
Noah took two of each kind.

Chapter 10: Generations again.
Chapter 11: A tower to heaven.

Chapter 12 through 25
Abraham and his three wives.

Twenty-six through twenty-eight Isaac and Rebekah, his mate,

Twenty-nine through thirty-six Jacob too is sadly tricked.

Thirty-seven through the end Joseph's brothers Jacob did send.

Fifty chapters has this book
And many lessons, if you'll look.

Study hard and you will see
A "very good" from Sue Crabtree

—Karen Pruitt

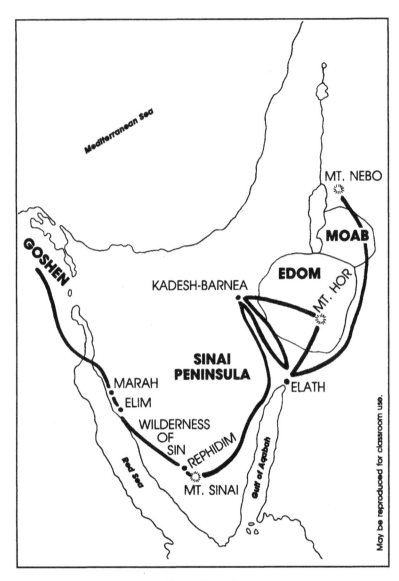

The Exodus

Chapter Two

Exodus

EXODUS—AN EXIT OUT OF EGYPT

In the first chapter of the book of Exodus the Israelites are made slaves in Egypt by the hand of Pharaoh. They remain in their bondage until Moses, God's humble servant, is commissioned to lead them out to a land of promise beyond the Jordan River. The story in Exodus is one of hope for the people but also of their disobedience. Moses leads them across the Red Sea, through the wilderness and on to Mt. Sinai. There they receive the Ten Commandments and build a tabernacle. Exodus is filled with adventure and teaches one about the power of the Almighty God.

FACT SHEET ON EXODUS

Exodus: means going out (children of Israel going out of Egypt)
written by Moses
*covers 200 or 400 years of history
has 40 chapters
begins with Israel being made slaves
ends with them encamped at Mt. Sinai

*In Exodus 12:40, the Bible says the bondage lasted 430 years. In Genesis 15:13, the writer says 400 years. Most historians think Egyptian bondage was about 200 years. The 400 years can be computed by counting from the time Abraham first went down to Egypt.

BRIEF OUTLINE OF EXODUS

Chapter/s	Event or Person/s
Ch. 1	Pharaoh made the Israelites slaves
2	Moses
3	Moses sees the burning bush
4-6	God gives Moses three signs to go before Pharaoh
7-11	Plagues
12	Feast of Passover, the Israelites leave Egypt
13-19	Journey from Egypt to Mt. Sinai
20	Ten Commandments
32-34	Story of golden calf
20-40	Commandments and laws, Instructions for building the tabernacle

CHARACTER LIST

Study characters in first column, then second, and then third.

A	B	C
Moses	Reuel or Jethro	Hur
Amram	Eleazar	Ithamar
Jochebed	Gershom	Bezaleel
Miriam	Eliezar	Aholiab
Aaron	Nadab	
Zipporah	Abihu	

MAP SEARCH

Journey from Egypt to Mt. Sinai
Trace the journey of Israel by finding these places on the map.

1. From Goshen in Egypt to Succoth. Ex. 12:37 (blood on door posts)

2. From Succoth to Etham. Ex. 13:20 (pillar to lead them)

3. From Etham to Pihahiroth. Ex. 14:2 (crossed the Red Sea)

4. From the crossing to Marah. Ex. 15:23 (bitter water made sweet)

5. From Marah to Elim. Ex. 15:27 (wells of water and palm trees)

6. Elim to Wilderness of Sin. Ex. 16:1 (manna and quails, Ex. 16:13-18)

7. Wilderness of Sin to Rephidim. Ex. 17:1-6 (water from smitten rock, Moses' hands supported at battle)

8. From Rephidim to Mt. Sinai. Ex. 19:1, 2. Moses received tables of stone, Ex. 19, 20. Tabernacle erected, Ex. 25–40. Golden calf was built, Ex. 32–34. Nadab and Abihu were killed, Lev. 10.

CHORAL READING
Just for Fun
PHARAOH AND THE PLAGUES
Exodus 7–12

Divide the class into two groups. Choose a person to read each of the special parts.

1st Person: Oh! The water turned to BLOOD, no water to drink,
                    And for seven whole days all Egypt did stink!

ALL: *CHORUS:*
                    Oh! Take this plague away and I'll let the people go.
                    'Twas the promise made by ole Pharaoh.

Group I: The Frogs did hop and the Lice and Flies did crawl:
                    And old Pharaoh didn't like it at all.

ALL: *CHORUS*

Group II: The Cows and the Horses and the Camels and the Sheep,
                    They all did Die and the people did weep.

ALL: *CHORUS*

2nd Person: Moses threw the ashes up into the air, And boils, boils, boils, everywhere.

ALL: *CHORUS*

Group I: Then it thundered, and there was lightning and Hail rained down,

(loud)   And it crushed all the crops and the trees to the ground.

ALL: *CHORUS*

Group II: Along came the Locusts and ate everything,
                    (Group I: z-z-z-z-z-z-z)
                    Til' not one blade of grass could be seen.

ALL:	*CHORUS*
3rd Person:	Then there was Darkness as black as could be,
	For three whole days the Egyptians couldn't see.
ALL:	*CHORUS*
4th Person:	The Death Angel passed over and the oldest child
	died.
	(Others: OO-OOO-OOO)
5th Person:	And Pharaoh broke down and sobbed and cried.
ALL:	*CHORUS* (softly and sad)

Author Unknown

Interesting Calculations About the Events in Exodus

- Exodus 12:37 states that there were 600,000 men, besides women and children. Multiply 600,000 by five to include women and children (a conservative figure), and that would mean Moses led three million people across the wilderness. (That's the population of a small state)
- Crossing the Red Sea in one night:
  A. If they went on a narrow path, double file, the line would be 800 miles long and would require 35 days and nights to get through.
  B. There had to be a space in the Red Sea, 3 miles wide, so that they could walk 5,000 abreast to get over in one night.
- Provisions and water Moses would need:
  A. 1,500 tons of food daily, which would require two freight trains each a mile long, each day.
  B. 4,000 tons of wood for cooking food: 3 freight trains, each a mile long, per day.
  C. 11,000 gallons each day to have enough water to drink and wash a few dishes.

- Campsite:
  Campsite each day, the size of 2/3 of the state of Rhode
  Island or 750 square miles, was needed.
- This was for 40 years.

Use a Stacking System to Remember the 10 Plagues

1.	Water to Blood	(Think of Nile River flowing with blood)
2.	Frogs	(Think of a big green frog floating down the Nile River)
3.	Lice	(Think of a little louse crawling on the back of the frog, tickling him)
4.	Flies	(Think of a fly with one leg on the louse and one long leg on a dead cow on the bank of the river)
5.	Murrain of Cattle	
6.	Boils	(Think of a big boil {sore} on the leg of the dead cow)
7.	Hail	(Think of the boil being packed in ice from the hail storm)
8.	Locust	(Think of a locust standing on top of the ice, shaking from the cold. He is so cold, he jumps to a dark room.)
9.	Darkness	
10.	Death of First Born	(Think of a dead child in the dark room)

SHORT ANSWER QUESTIONS ABOUT EXODUS

1. Exodus means _____.

2. Exodus covers _____ years.

3. The story in Exodus is about _____.

4. The book begins with the children of Israel in _____.

5. The book closes with the children of Israel at _____.

6. Three signs God gave Moses are _____, _____, and _____.

7. Moses' father: _____

8. Moses' mother: _____

9. Moses' sons: _____ and _____

10. Moses' wife: _____

11. Moses' brother and sister: _____ and _____

12. Moses' father-in-law: _____

13. Aaron's four sons: _____, _____, _____, _____

14. Name the ten plagues. (Exodus 7–11)

15. Name the Ten Commandments. (Exodus 20)

THOUGHT QUESTIONS

1. Give a description of Jochebed. What lessons can we learn from her?

2. In Numbers 12:3, God says Moses was the meekest man on the face of the earth. What is meekness? How was Moses meek? How can we develop meekness?

SPECIAL CHALLENGES

For volunteers only. Choose one or more to do this week.

1. Memorize the outline of Exodus.
2. Be able to identify the characters in Exodus.
3. Memorize the ten plagues and the Ten Commandments.
4. Make a list of ten lessons you can learn from Exodus.
5. Write a song or poem about the events in Exodus.
6. Make a mural of the plagues or Ten Commandments (can be a fun class project).
7. Research the three Jewish feast days: Passover, Pentecost, and Feast of Tabernacles.
8. Make a model of a tabernacle.

APPLICATION

In Exodus 16, the words "murmur" or "complain" are used eight times. The children of Israel murmured and complained even though God was taking care of them. It is easy to condemn the Israelites, but what about us? In what ways are we like the Israelites? In what ways are we blessed more than the Israelites and more than many other countries of the world? What things do we complain about? Read Philippians 4:11 and make application to your life.

Make a complaint chart, and this week put a check on it every time you complain. We often complain without thinking about it. Let's not be ungrateful like the children of Israel.

SUGGESTIONS FOR TEACHING

Sharing: The children of Israel complained about circumstances, food, and water. Sometimes we forget our blessings. Name one thing (not person) that you are thankful for today.

Prayer:

Review from last lesson

Options: 1. Review fact sheets, answer questions, trace journey on the map and talk about application.

2. Teacher or student reviews the history of Exodus, using a map to show the journey from Egypt to Mt. Sinai. Students can trace the journey with yarn or colored pencils on their individual maps.

3. Have students report on the characters and make application to each of our lives.

4. Do a study of the Ten Commandments and make a search to find nine of them in the New Testament.

5. Encourage those who volunteer to meet the challenges and share those with the class.

6. Encourage the reading of the book of Exodus, especially chapters 1–20, 32, 33.

Share thoughts with the class.

Remember: the more participation, the more learning takes place.

Exodus

The Israelites became slaves in Egypt, we know.
Then God spoke to Moses saying, "To Pharaoh you must go."
Moses found reasons to resist
But God had a plan and to Moses He did insist.

For each excuse there was a solution
And Aaron was drafted for his elocution.
So Moses left from Midian with his sons and his wife
To begin the third phase of his varied life.

With signs to confirm his direction from God
A serpent appeared when he cast down his rod
Pharaoh needed these slaves who could make bricks and build a city
So he increased their work and had no pity.

The children of Israel despaired, crying and weak.
They listened not to Moses' assurances
For they focused only on their own endurances.
But Moses and Aaron did as they were told
And again approached Pharaoh, feeling a little less bold.

And the waters ran red as blood sent by God
Not one plague but ten had to be sent
Before Pharaoh, the king, did ever relent.

Though frogs and lice and flies he resisted
After dead cows and boils, hail and locust visited.
Darkness fell next but the worst still awaited
When all firstborn died, they were at last emancipated.

They were urged by the Egyptians to go and worship this One
Whose will Pharaoh's people had witnessed being done.
And so the multitude started out walking that night
With the spoils of Egypt given as their right.

Before it could rise, their dough they did take
And when hunger came up on them, unleavened cakes they did bake.
Saying this Passover must be remembered and observed every year.
And instructions were given for those to recall
The events of this day as a remembrance for all.

—Faye Gibson

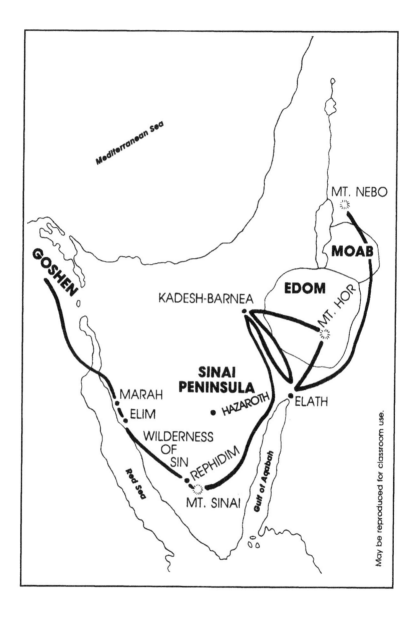

Mediterranean Sea

MT. NEBO

GOSHEN

MOAB

EDOM

KADESH-BARNEA

MT. HOR

SINAI
PENINSULA

MARAH

ELIM

HAZAROTH

ELATH

WILDERNESS
OF
SIN

REPHIDIM

Red Sea

Gulf of Aqabah

MT. SINAI

May be reproduced for classroom use.

Chapter Three

Leviticus, Numbers

FACT SHEET ON LEVITICUS

Leviticus: A book about the Jewish laws and the duties of the
priests. Four chapters of interest are:
Chapter 10   Nadab and Abihu
Chapter 11   Characteristics of clean and unclean
animals
Chapter 23   Discussion of Passover, Pentecost
and Feast of Tabernacles
Chapter 24   Man is stoned for blasphemy

THE BOOK OF NUMBERS

Numbers—A Book of Counting and Wandering

The book of Numbers begins with the Israelites at Mt. Sinai
where they are counted. Moses continued to lead them through the
wilderness and on to Kadesh-Barnea. After twelve spies return and
ten bring a sad report, God decides they will not be able to enter the

promised land. The people die in the wilderness and Moses brings their children up to the land of Moab, where they are counted again. The book is one of frustration for a people who have not made peace with their God.

FACT SHEET ON NUMBERS

Numbers

<u>named</u> Numbers because the people of God were numbered twice in the book (1, 36)
<u>written</u> by Moses
<u>covers</u> 40 years of Bible history
<u>has</u> 36 chapters
<u>begins</u> with the children of Israel at Mt. Sinai
<u>ends</u> with Israelites encamped in the Plains of Moab, ready to go into the promised land

*OUTLINE OF NUMBERS

Chapter/s	Event or Person/s
Ch. 1	Numbering: 603, 550 males (Mt. Sinai)
11	People complain about the manna, God sends quail
12	Miriam and Aaron speak against Moses
13, 14	Spies and their report
16, 17	Korah's rebellion—Aaron's rod budded
20	Moses' sin—Aaron dies
21	Fiery serpents are sent out
22–24	Balak and Baalam
26	Numbering: 601,730 males (Moab)

*Some chapters which contain laws and instructions are omitted.

CHARACTER LIST

Joshua	Balaam	Kohath
Balak	Caleb	Merari
	Korah	Gershon
		Dathan

MAP SEARCH

Find the places where the Israelites stopped on the journey to Canaan on the Exodus map. Make a note on the map or draw an illustration to show what occurred at the place.

JOURNEY FROM MT. SINAI TO CANAAN

Mt. Sinai
- A. Ten Commandments and other commandments are given (Exodus)
- B. Golden calf is built (Exodus)
- C. Built the tabernacle (Exodus)
- D. Nadab and Abihu die (Lev. 10)
- E. People are numbered (Numbers 1)

Wilderness of Paran (chapter 11)
- A. People complained, God sent fire
- B. Quail is given
- C. God plagued them

Hazeroth: Aaron and Miriam speak against Moses for his Ethiopian wife (chapter 12)

Kadesh-Barnea
   A. Spies are sent out (chapter 13)
   B. Man that broke the Sabbath was stoned (chapter 15)
   C. Korah's rebellion (chapter 16)
   D. Aaron's rod budded (chapter 17)
   E. Moses' sin (chapter 20)

Mt. Hor
   A. Aaron dies (chapter 20)
   B. Eleazar becomes priest

Edom
   A. Edom refused passage (chapter 20)
   B. Fiery serpents are sent out (chapter 21)
   C. Defeated Ammon (chapter 21)

Plains of Moab
   A. Baalam and Balak (chapter 22-24)
   B. Israelites commit whoredom with Moab (chapter 25)
   C. Second numbering (chapter 26)

Mt. Nebo (Deuteronomy 34)
   A. Moses views promised land
   B. Moses dies there

COMPARISON OF THE NUMBERINGS IN NUMBERS 1 AND NUMBERS 26

	Ch. 1	Ch. 26
Reuben	46,500	43,730
Simeon	59,300	22,200
Gad	45,650	45,500
Judah	74,600	76,500
Issachar	54,400	64,300
Zebulun	57,400	60,500
Ephraim	40,500	32,500
Manasseh	32,200	52,700
Benjamin	35,400	45,600
Dan	62,700	64,400
Asher	41,500	53,400
Naphtali	53,400	45,400
	603,550 Total	**601,730 Total**

SOME FACTS CONCERNING THE TRIBES

- There was no tribe of Joseph. Instead, his two sons, Ephraim and Manasseh, were heads of tribes.
- Counting Joseph's sons, there were actually 13 tribes.
- The Levites were the priestly tribe. They received no land grant but instead lived in 48 cities assigned to them. They were not counted in the number.
- Judah was always the strongest tribe. Christ came through Judah's lineage.
- Lots were cast to assign the various tribes to their land grants in the new land.

SHORT ANSWER QUESTIONS ON NUMBERS

1. Aaron and Miriam spoke against Moses because _____
   _____.

2. _____ developed a case of leprosy as a result
   of speaking against Moses.

3. _____ and _____ were the two good spies.

4. How did Korah and his men die? _____

5. Aaron's rod budded _____ to show that God had
   chosen Aaron.

6. The prophet of God hired by the king of Moab to curse Israel
   was _____.

7. The king of Moab was _____.

8. Aaron died at _____.

9. The spies' report about the new land was _____
   _____.

10. The children of Israel wandered in the wilderness for forty
    years because _____.

THOUGHT QUESTIONS

1. Moses' life can be divided into three periods: 40 years in the palace, 40 years in the wilderness as a shepherd, 40 years leading Israel. Discuss characteristics of Moses during these three periods. Why was he such a great man?

2. Why were the Israelites ungrateful to God? Discuss some of their punishments. Do you see any similarities between these Jews and people today? How does God punish us today?

SPECIAL CHALLENGES

For volunteers only. Complete one or two challenges this week.

1. Memorize an outline of Numbers.
2. Be able to identify the characters in the book.
3. Make a list of seven lessons you can learn from Leviticus and Numbers.
4. Write a song or poem about events in Numbers.
5. Make a model of the brass serpent in chapter 21 to remind others that we must look to God to be cleansed.
6. Role play the story of Korah (chapter 16) or the fiery serpents (chapter 21) or Baalam and Balak (chapters 22–24).
7. Make a chart, comparing the numbering in chapter 1 and the numbering in chapter 26.

APPLICATION—Numbers 13 and 14

One of the inspirational stories in Numbers is the story of Joshua and Caleb in chapter 13. Two out of twelve stood for truth. They were in the minority and yet they did not give in. They rent their clothes and cried unto the people that God would give them the land. How many times do we stand for truth and what is right when the wrong is popular? How many times have we chosen the wrong way because everyone else has chosen it, has said it, or is going there? It takes a strong individual to stand for the right when the wrong is popular. Discuss ways we develop this strength. Give examples of times when you stood with a minority for good.

SUGGESTIONS FOR TEACHING

Sharing: Miriam and Aaron spoke against Moses. Name one good thing about one of your brothers or sisters and share it with the class.

Prayer:

Review from last lesson

Options: 1. Review fact sheet, answer questions, trace the journey on a map, talk about application.

2. Teacher or student reviews the history in Numbers, using a map to show places.

3. Have students report on the characters and make application.

4. Encourage those who have accepted the challenges to share them with the class.

5. Encourage the reading of Numbers outside of class and sharing thoughts with the class.

6. Role play suggested stories listed under the challenge.

7. Have six different people report on the six main stories in Numbers:

Miriam and Aaron speak against Moses
Spies and their report
Korah's rebellion
Moses' sin
Fiery snakes
Baalam and Balak

Be sure to give some application from these stories.
(This suggestion will probably take about 45 minutes.)

Remember: the more participation, the more learning takes place.

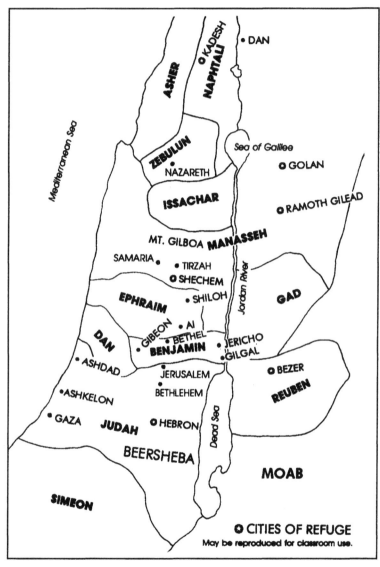

Dividing the land among the tribes

Chapter Four

Deuteronomy, Joshua

DEUTERONOMY—A REPEAT OF HISTORY

When the Israelites arrive in Moab, Moses makes a speech to them about their faithful and unfaithful service to God. He repeats the Ten Commandments and other laws. In the last chapter of this book, the Lord gives the events of Moses' death upon Mt. Nebo. The book is a further proclamation of God's power and sovereignty.

JOSHUA—THE CONQUEST OF CANAAN

Joshua takes Moses' place and leads the people into the promised land. God has given them the land but they must conquer it. They move across the Jordan, take Jericho and Ai and move to the north: All the land is divided among the twelve tribes, and the Levites are given 48 cities scattered throughout the country. Joshua was a great leader, fearing and obeying the voice of God.

FACT SHEET ON JOSHUA
The Story of the Conquest of Canaan

tells the story of the conquest of Canaan
named for the main character and leader
written by Joshua
covers 40 years of Bible history
has 24 chapters
begins with children of Israel in the Plains of Moab ready
to march into Canaan
ends with land being divided among the twelve tribes

OUTLINE OF JOSHUA

Ch. 1	Joshua takes command
2	Spies are sent to Jericho, Rahab hides them
3	Israelites cross Jordan
4	12 stones are set up at Gilgal and the crossing
5	Israelites were circumcised
	They kept the passover at Gilgal
	Captain of host appears to Joshua
6	Joshua takes Jericho
7	Israel is defeated at Ai because of Achan
8	Achan is burned—people at Ai are destroyed.
9	Gibeonites make a league with Joshua
10	Joshua fights five kings (sun and moon stood still)
11	Israel takes northern Canaan
12, 13	Land is divided
20	Six cities of refuge
21-23	Instructions are given
24	Joshua's farewell address

CHARACTER LIST

Joshua
Nun
Rahab
Achan
Gibeonites
Eleazar
Phinehas

MAP SEARCH

Jericho
Ai
Gilgal
Shiloh

Six cities of refuge
1. Kadesh   4. Bezer
2. Shechem   5. Ramoth
3. Hebron   6. Golan

SHORT ANSWER QUESTIONS

1. The Ten Commandments are recorded in _____ book/chapter) and _____ (book/chapter).

2. Joshua's father was _____.

3. _____ hid the spies in Jericho and made the following request of them: _____ _____.

4. How did the walls fall down at Jericho? _____ _____.

5. Achan stole _____ at Jericho.

6. The people were defeated at Ai because _____.

7. What did the Gibeonites do?_____
   _____.

8. What did Joshua do when the day wasn't long enough to win the battle? _____.

9. What was the purpose of the cities of refuge? _____
   _____

10. How did Joshua decide how the land would be divided?
    _____.

THOUGHT QUESTIONS

1. The Bible says the people served the Lord all the days of Joshua and all the days of the elders that outlived Joshua. No sin against Joshua is recorded in the Bible. Describe someone today who inspires others to live for the Lord. Name some of their characteristics that you would like to possess.

2. Summarize Joshua's farewell address given in Joshua 24. If one were giving an address today to the church or his family, what would he say?

SPECIAL CHALLENGES

For volunteers only. Choose one or more you would like to do this week.

1. Memorize the outline of Joshua.
2. Be able to identify all the characters.
3. Locate all the places on the map and the significance of each place.
4. Be able to name the 13 tribes.
5. Memorize Joshua 24:15
6. To the tune of "Three Blind Mice" write a song about the conquest of Canaan.
7. Make a list of eight good characteristics of Joshua.

APPLICATION—Joshua 2

Rahab had faith in Jehovah God and believed that He would destroy Jericho. She asked the spies to spare not only her life, but also the lives of her family. Because of this, she is in the lineage of Christ. There are two major lessons here.

1. God will forgive you and wipe your slate clean no matter what you have done in the past. Rahab was a harlot who was forgiven and married Salmon and begat Boaz. Boaz married Ruth and was the great-grandfather of David. Forget your past sins like Rahab and begin to live a free life in Christ. Have you done what the Lord requires to be free from those sins? Have you forgiven yourself of your mistake?

2. When we come to know the Lord, we should be concerned about our families as Rahab was. She wanted to make sure they were saved. What have we done for the salvation of our family? What can we do if they won't listen to the gospel? What can we do this week?

SUGGESTIONS FOR TEACHING

Sharing: Joshua was a great leader for the Lord. Name one way you can be a leader for God.

Prayer:

Review from last lesson

Options: 1. Review fact sheets, answer questions, find places on the map and talk about application.
2. Make a flip chart of the stories in Joshua on poster paper (you can draw stick figures) or on overhead transparencies and tell the stories as you show the pictures. (Use the outline of Joshua to make the flip chart.)

Remember: the more participation, the more learning takes place

Joshua

When Moses died, he left a space
So God put Joshua in that place.
The promised land was now quite near.
And the Lord told Joshua not to fear.

He said with him He would be
Just follow His commands and all would see.
Joshua obeyed that he was told to do
And soon dispatched two spies to view.

The city of Jericho and the land around
And with Rahab's help they were not found.
Though walled, Jericho could not stand
When Joshua led Israel with the help of God's Hand.

After marching silently around the city six days in a row
On the seventh, six times, then a seventh they did go.
The trumpets sounded and with a mighty roar
God's people had no need to even open a door.

For the walls fell flat and the people were taken
As their belongings and treasures were quickly forsaken.
Only Rahab and her family were left to survive
For hiding the spies, they did not lose their lives.

Spoils were forbidden, save for the Lord, we are told
But Achan became greedy and took silver and gold.
Because of his disobedience the next battle was lost
The defeat by Ai came at a great cost.

(continued)

God's anger descended upon the children of Israel that day,
And Joshua knew the offender had to pay.
Following instructions, Achan was finally selected
Though his sin he admitted, swift punishment wasn't neglected.

God allowed Joshua then another try
And by waiting on God, Joshua's men took Ai.
The city they seized and then set afire
All men were killed and the city gate came the king's bier.

An altar was built with stones as written in the book of the law.
In mount Ebal with sacrifices to God, Joshua made sure Israel
saw.
Then the Gibeonites met and developed a plot.
They dressed as weary travelers who were down on their lot.

They approached Joshua and asked for protection for them all.
And Joshua agreed without the Lord making this call.
Next came an attack by the Amorites that continued until
It was obvious more time was needed and the sun stood still.

When victory was theirs, the sun finally did set
But never in time was this precedent met.
The battles continue and Joshua holds to God's Plan
And finally at last they come to the Promised Land!

The land is divided
Cities of refuge provided.
Joshua's farewell address offered
Exhortations of faithfulness proffered.
Then Joshua dies at a hundred and ten
His legacy rich before God and men.

—Faye Gibson

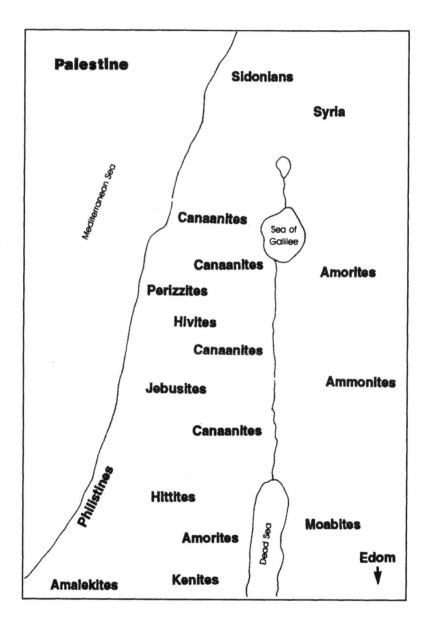

Chapter Five

Judges, Ruth

JUDGES—DELIVERANCE FROM THE ENEMY

The people would sin and turn away from God and serve other gods. Their enemies from the land would overcome them, and they would cry to God. He would raise up a judge who would deliver them from their enemies. The land would have rest, and then the judge would die, and the people would sin again. This cycle continued for 400 years, with fifteen judges leading the people. This book of conquest has twenty-one chapters.

FACT SHEET ON JUDGES

covers 400 years of Bible history
has 21 chapters

OUTLINE OF THE PERIOD
OF THE JUDGES

I.   Continued conquest of Canaan after Joshua. 1:1-36

II.   Summary of Israel's apostasy. 2:1—3:6

    A. Angel rebukes Israel for breaking covenant; Israel weeps (2:1-5)

    B. Account of Israel's loyalty under Joshua and Elders. (2:6-10)

    C. The cycle of apostasy in Israel's history.

        1. Israel did evil and served other gods. (2:11-13)

        2. Jehovah angered; people oppressed by their enemies. (2:14, 15)

        3. Israel cried; Judges delivered them. (2:16-18)

        4. Upon the judge's death, Israel sinned more corruptly; Jehovah angered. (2:19, 20)

        5. Jehovah left wicked nations to prove and afflict Israel (2:21–3:6)

III.   Individual Judges and events concerning them (3:7–16:31)

	Judges	Oppressors	Rest	Reference
1.	Othniel	Chushanrishathaim King of Mesopotamia	40	3:7-11
2.	Ehud	Eglon of Moab	80	3:12-30
3.	Shamgar	Philistines		3:31
4.	Deborah (Barak)	Jabin of Canaan (Captain Sisera)	40	4:1–5:31
5.	Gideon	Midian	40	6:1–8:28
6.	Abimelech		3	8:29–9:57
7.	Tola		23	10:1, 2
8.	Jair		22	10:3-5
9.	Jephthah	Philistines & Ammon	6	10:6–12:7
10.	Ibzan		7	12:8-10
11.	Elon		10	12:11, 12

	Judges	Oppressors	Rest	Reference
12.	Abdon		8	12:13-15
13.	Samson	Philistines	20	13:1–16:31
14.	*Eli	Philistines	40	1 Sam. 1–4:2
15.	*Samuel	Philistines		1 Sam. 1–7:1

* Read about in 1 Samuel

Events related to the period of the Judges
- A. Micah, his image and priest, and the Danites. 17:1–18:31
- B. The Levite, his concubine, and civil war between Benjamin and Israel. (19:1–21:25)
- C. The Book of Ruth. Ruth (1:1–4:22)

CHARACTER LIST

15 Judges	King Eglon	Delilah
Barak	Heber	Manoah
Jabin	Jael	
Sisera		

MAP SEARCH

Mesopotamia	Midian
Moab	Ammon
Philistia	Canaan

SONG ABOUT THE JUDGES
(Tune: Reuben, Reuben)

God set jud-ges over Is-rael
One brave wo-man, four-teen men.
They helped Is-rael fight their bat-tles,
Led them back to God from sin.

Oth-niel, E-hud, Sham-gar, Debo-rah,
Gid-eon, Abim-e-lech, To-la, Jair,
Jeph-thah, Ib-zan, E-lon, Ab-don,
Sam-son, E-li, Sam-u-el.

Author Unknown

RUTH

Ruth is a short book of four chapters about a Moabitish woman
who is in the lineage of Christ. This story took place during the time
of the judges. Generations from Judah to David are named in the
last chapter.

CHARACTER LIST

Elimelech	Mahlon	Boaz
Naomi	Chilion	Obed
Ruth	Orphah	

Generations in the lineage of Christ (Ruth 4:18-22)

Abraham, Isaac, Jacob, Judah, Pharez, Hezron, Ram,
Amminadab, Nahshon, Salmon, Boaz, Obed, Jesse, David

SHORT ANSWER: Joshua, Judges, Ruth (Who Am I?)

1. _____ I made a rash vow.

2. _____ I fought the Midianites with 300 men.

3. _____ I was a left-handed judge.

4. _____ I was the son of Manoah.

5. _____ I was the son of Nun.

6. _____ I had a helper named Barak.

7. _____ I stole some things at Jericho.

8. _____ I was a judge who married a Philistine.

9. _____ God gave me the sign of the fleece.

10. _____ I was a captain who had a tent nail driven through my temple.

11. _____ I killed 600 Philistines with an ox goad.

12. _____ I set 300 foxes' tails on fire.

13. _____ I was a harlot who hid the spies at Jericho.

14. _____ I was a woman who killed the captain of the Canaanite army.

15. _____ I was the king of Moab.

16._____ I killed 1000 Philistines with the jawbone of an ass.

17._____ My daughter-in-law was Ruth.

18._____ I was the son of Ruth.

19._____ I was the second husband of Ruth.

20._____ I was a husband to Naomi.

THOUGHT QUESTIONS

1. Samson's downfall was a Philistine woman. What would make a man of God want a heathen wife? Does this happen today? What can we do to encourage our children to marry Christians?

2. Ruth was devoted to her mother-in-law, Naomi. They were close friends. What makes a good relationship between mothers-in-law and daughters-in-law? Make a list of do's and don't's for mothers-in-law.

SPECIAL CHALLENGES

1. Memorize the names of the fifteen judges in order. (You can use the song.)
2. Be able to identify the characters in Judges and Ruth.
3. Be able to name the generations from Abraham to David. (Ruth 4:18-23)
4. Read the books of Judges and Ruth this week.

APPLICATION

Deborah was a judge, a leader of God's people. There are many ways that women can be leaders for God today. Discuss the following and add to the list:

- Make a suggestion to the elders
- Assist husband in his work for the church
- Have a Bible study in your home
- Grade correspondence courses
- Teach ladies' and children's classes
- Help plan a women's program at the church under the elders' leadership
- Work in organizing materials for the church
- Teach the younger women
- Be a good wife and mother

SUGGESTIONS FOR TEACHING

Sharing: The period during the judges was a dark period in the history of God's people. God allowed these people to be overcome by their enemies because of sin. Today many people have dark periods in their lives that may or may not be caused by sin. Name some things in our lives that cause us discouragement. Be sure to end the discussion by talking about all spiritual blessings in Christ. (Eph. 1:3)

Prayer:

Review from last lesson

Options: 1. Review from last lesson.
2. Teacher tells the narrative stories of the judges. (Some are less familiar.) Students can take notes, outline, and so on. Find Israel's oppressors on the map given.
3. Have students report on the following judges: Ehud, Deborah, Gideon, Jephthah, Samson. Encourage them to give application lessons on these judges.
4. Encourage those who accepted the challenges to share them with the class.
5. Encourage the reading of Judges and Ruth outside class and sharing thoughts with the class.

Remember: the more participation, the more learning takes place

Naomi Remembers

I was left alone in a foreign land
Being guided only by God's Sovereign Hand.
With my two daughters-in-law by my side,
The tears I shed, I could not hide.
Two and three times I petitioned them to go home;
Orpah returned and Ruth became my own.

With Bethlehem now in sight,
The joy we were greeted with filled me with spite.
To be known as "Naomi," I could not bear.
I called myself "Mara," for none of it was fair.

In a field of barley, Ruth asked to glean.
The master of which remained to be seen.
Boaz, the owner, was a man in great standing
Gave her access and was not demanding.

"Blessed be he who looks at you kindly!
Go, my child, uncover his feet and do so blindly.
He knows you are a virtuous woman; so do not fear.
This day the matter will be sealed; so, to me, hold near."

The one who was closer relinquished his right.
A sandal was passed before it was night.
Ruth's kinsman-redeemer, Boaz became
Then joy and happiness replaced all my pain.

—Chris Hubbard

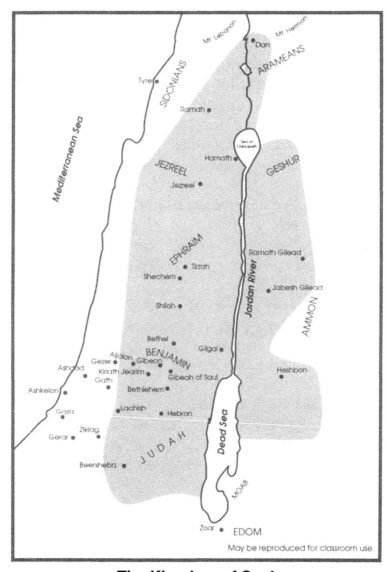

The Kingdom of Saul

Chapter Six

1 Samuel

1 SAMUEL—THE ISRAELITES GET A KING

Samuel was the last judge and his sons were wicked. The people wanted a king and God gave them Saul. This is a book about the life of Saul as king. The events in the life of David as a young man are also recorded. Stories of war, Michal and Jonathan, Saul's children and Saul's departure from God make this book an interesting one.

FACT SHEET ON 1 SAMUEL

The United Kingdom was a period in Israel's history in which all the people were united together under one king. It covers 120 years.

Saul's Reign	40 years	1 Samuel
David's Reign	40 years	2 Samuel
Solomon's Reign	40 years	1 Kings 1–11
Total:	120 years	

1 Samuel: <u>written</u> by Samuel, a judge, prophet, and priest
<u>covers</u> 40 years of Bible history
<u>has</u> 31 chapters
<u>begins</u> with Eli, the judge
<u>ends</u> with the death of Saul and his sons

OUTLINE OF 1 SAMUEL

I. Eli as priest and judge—chapters 1–4
   A. Birth of Samuel
   B. Tabernacle service
   C. Two warnings to Eli
   D. Judgment on Eli

II. Samuel as prophet, priest and judge—chapters 5–8
   A. The ark restored to Israel
   B. Revival and victory
   C. Summary of Samuel's ministry
   D. Request for a king

III. Leadership transferred to Saul—chapters 9–12
   A. Samuel anoints Saul privately
   B. Victory over the Ammonites
   C. Saul chosen by Israel
   D. Saul's public inauguration

IV. National victories and personal failures—chapters 13–15
   A. Saul fails to wait for Samuel
   B. Philistines defeated at Michmash
   C. Surrounding nations subdued
   D. Disobedience in an Amalekite victory

V. Saul the king and David the fugitive—chapters 16–26
   A. David's rise to national fame
   B. Saul seeks to ensnare David
   C. Friendship of David and Jonathan
   D. David's flight and its consequences
   E. Saul's pursuit of David

VI. The Philistine-Israelite conflict—chapters 27–31
   A. Philistines afford David refuge
   B. Saul seeks help in Endor from a witch
   C. David recovers his possessions
   D. Death of Saul and his sons

SUGGESTED STORIES TO NOTE

Chapter/s	Event or Person/s
Ch. 1-3	Hannah and Samuel
9	Saul is chosen
13	Saul's sin at Michmash
15	Saul's sin against Amalek
17	David and Goliath
18	Michal is given to David
24	David spares Saul's life
25	Abigail and David
28	Witch of Endor
31	Death of Saul

CHARACTER LIST

Elkanah	Michal
Hannah	Abigail
Peninnah	Abner
Eli	Witch of Endor
Samuel	Ahinoam, wife of Saul (14:50)
Saul	Ahinoam, wife of David (25:43)
Kish	King Agag
Jonathan	Goliath
Jesse	

REIGN OF SAUL—OUTLINE

1. Saul chosen as king
2. Saul anointed
3. Saul's disobedience
4. David anointed secretly
5. David and Goliath
6. David in Saul's court
7. David marries Michal, Saul's daughter
8. David and Jonathan, Saul's son
9. David flees from Saul
10. Saul requests the witch of Endor to bring Samuel from the dead
11. Death of Saul and sons

SHORT ANSWER QUESTIONS

1. The Amalekite king that Saul saved was _____.

2. Captain of Saul's army was _____.

3. Saul's two great sins were (ch. 13, 15) _____
    _____.

4. Woman who raised Samuel from the dead: _____

5. _____, a judge, priest, and prophet.

6. Saul reigned for _____ years.

7. Saul was the son of _____.

8. Why did the people want a king? _____
    _____

9. Woman who was married to Nabal and later to David was

    _____.

10. Samuel's mother and father were _____ and

    _____.

11. _____, Saul's daughter.

12. _____, Saul's son, David's friend.

13. _____, the priest with whom Samuel lived
    in the temple.

14. _____ was the nation that Israel was fighting.

THOUGHT QUESTIONS

1. Saul had a problem with pride. He didn't want others to have
   more power than he had. In what ways do we have problems
   with pride today? Are members of the church jealous of one
   another? What can we do to overcome the sin of pride?

2. Why do you think God described David as "a man after His own
   heart" (1 Sam. 13:4)? What characteristics did David possess that
   we would like to emulate? Would God describe us as persons after
   His own heart? Why or why not?

SPECIAL CHALLENGES

1. Practice being a storyteller and learn to tell some of the stories in 1 Samuel.
2. Be able to identify the characters in the book of 1 Samuel.
3. Memory verse: 1 Samuel 15:22
4. Draw a mural (you may use stick figures) of the events in Abigail's life as recorded in 1 Samuel 25.
5. Be able to describe the events listed in the stories under "Suggested Stories To Note."
6. Write a song about David killing the giant to the tune of "Row, Row, Row Your Boat."

APPLICATION—1 Samuel 25

Abigail is often described as a woman who married the wrong man. She was a beautiful, good woman. She was married to a cruel and evil man, a drunk. Even though her husband was wicked, she continued to do right in the eyes of God. Does this have implications for a woman who is married to a cruel man today? Should a good woman stay with an evil husband? What if he forbids her to attend worship? What if he physically abuses her? What can we do to encourage good relationships in the home today?

SUGGESTIONS FOR TEACHING

Sharing: Jonathan was David's good friend. Name a characteristic of a good friend.

Prayer:

Options: 1. Review

2. Teacher or student tell some of the stories in 1 Samuel and make application.

3. Emphasize the importance of the United Kingdom, the reign of Saul and how these stories fit in the history of the Jews.

4. Let students practice storytelling by telling the stories of 1 Samuel.

5. Encourage the reading of 1 Samuel outside class and sharing thoughts with the class.

6. Let those who complete the challenges share them with the class.

Remember: the more participation, the more learning takes place

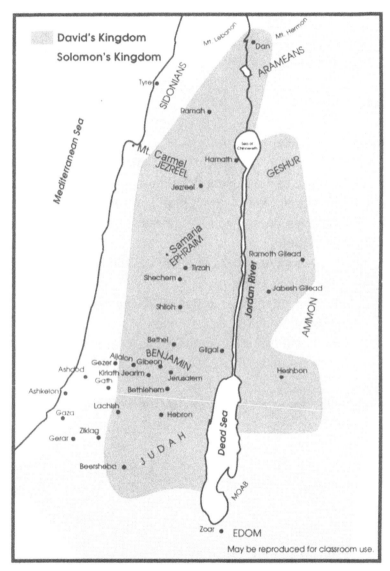

The Empire of David and Solomon

Chapter Seven

2 Samuel, 1 Kings 1–11

2 SAMUEL—"A MAN AFTER GOD'S OWN HEART"

This book is the story of David as king. Even though he was a great warrior and leader, David made many mistakes. He is called "a man after God's own heart" and the reader delves into the book to get some insight into his heart. Many characters are named and many events are given. A class could spend an entire year studying this period.

FACT SHEET ON 2 SAMUEL

written by Samuel
covers 40 years of Bible history
has 24 chapters
begins with David's becoming king
ends with David's sin in numbering the people

OUTLINE (2 SAMUEL)

Chapter:
1. David hears of Saul's death; has Amalekite killed
2. David is made king over Judah; Ishbosheth is king of the other eleven tribes; Abner and Joab fight; Abner kills Asahel
3. Abner comes to make peace with David; is slain by Joab; Michal is given back to David
4. Ishbosheth is killed by his own people; David has men slain
5. David is anointed king over all Israel; David smites the Philistines
6. David goes to bring the ark up; Uzzah is slain; Michal is made barren
7. David wants to build a house; praises God
8. David subdues his enemies
9. Kindness is shown to Mephibosheth
10. Ammonites and Syrians are defeated by Israel
11. David sins with Bathsheba
12. Nathan tells David that he is the one who has sinned; his son dies; "sword will not depart" from David's house
13. Amnon rapes Tamar; Absalom kills Amnon
14. Wise woman comes to David; David requests Absalom to come home after 3 years; reunion two years later
15. Absalom takes over; David flees
16. Ziba tells a lie; Shimei curses David
17. Ahithophel and Hushai counsel Absalom; Ahithophel hangs himself
18. War between David and Absalom; Joab kills Absalom
19. David comes home to Jerusalem
20. Sheba's rebellion; Joab kills Amasa, end of rebellion
21. Three years famine; seven descendants of Saul are killed
22. David's song of praise
23. David's last words; list of 37 mighty men
24. David sins in numbering the people; offers sacrifice

SUGGESTED STORIES TO NOTE

Many of these stories will not be familiar to most church members. However, there are many lessons to be learned from David. These stories are good for storytelling.

Chapter 6:   David brings ark and Uzziah is slain
Chapter 11:   David sins with Bathsheba
Chapter 12:   Nathan tells David a story and proclaims, "Thou art the man." David's punishment
Chapter 13:   Amnon rapes Tamar; Absalom kills Amnon
Chapter 14:   Wise woman comes to David; David brings Absalom home
Chapter 15:   Absalom tries to take over the kingdom
Chapter 18:   War between David and Absalom; Joab kills Absalom
Chapter 24:   David's sin in numbering the people

CHARACTERS FROM 2 SAMUEL

1. Ishbothsheth—son of Saul, made king after Saul's death
2. Joab—captain of David's army
3. Joab
   Abishai   three nephews of David
   Asahel
4. Amnon
   Absalom   sons of David
   Adonijah
   Solomon
5. Mephibosheth—son of Jonathan, lame, favored by David
6. Abinadab—a Levite in whose house the ark stayed for 20 years
7. Uzzah—touched the ark, God struck him
8. Gad—prophet
   Nathan—prophet

9. Ahimelech—priest
   Zadok—priest
10. Ziba—servant to Mephibosheth, house of Saul
11. Bathsheba—wife of Uriah and David
12. Tamar—daughter of David, sister of Absalom, raped by Amnon
13. Wise woman of Tekoah—employed by Joab, goes to David to get him to bring Absalom back
14. Ahithophel— counselor to Absalom
15. Hushai—counselor to Absalom, (David's friend, counseled against Absalom)
16. Shimei—man that cursed David as he was leaving Jerusalem
17. Amasa—captain of Absalom's host, became captain of David's host, slain by Joab
18. Sheba—led Israel in a rebellion against David
19. Rizpah—concubine of Saul, watchful over 2 sons when they were killed.

THE REIGN OF DAVID

1. David at Hebron
2. David at Jerusalem
3. The Ark is brought to Jerusalem
4. The sin of David with Bathsheba
5. Rebellion of Absalom
6. Last days and death of David

1 KINGS
Chapters 1–11

A RICH AND WISE/UNWISE MAN

This section of Kings records the events in the life of Solomon. God gives him a choice and he chooses an understanding heart. Thus he receives wisdom, power and riches. Toward the end of his life, he turns his heart away from God and builds idols. Solomon wrote Song of Solomon, Ecclesiastes and most of Proverbs.

FACT SHEET ON 1 KINGS 1–11

story of King Solomon
covers 40 years
begins with Solomon's becoming king
ends with Solomon's death

OUTLINE OF 1 KINGS 1–11
(KING SOLOMON)

Chapter 1:   Solomon is selected to be king
Chapter 2:   David dies
Chapter 3:   Solomon asks for an understanding heart (wisdom) to judge the people
Chapter 4:   Solomon's riches and possessions
Chapter 5:   Hiram, King of Tyre, gives Solomon cedars
Chapters 6–8: Solomon builds the temple (7 1/2 years in building) and his own palace (13 years in building)
Chapter 9:   Dedication of the temple (see 2 Chronicles 7)
Chapter 10:   Queen of Sheba visits Solomon
Chapter 11:   Solomon marries many strange women, sins, dies

CHARACTER LIST FOR 1 KINGS 1-11

Solomon	King Hiram
Nathan	Queen of Sheba
Bathsheba	700 wives, 300 concubines
Adonijah	(Many others)

MAP SEARCH

Tribe of Benjamin (Saul)
Tribe of Judah (David & Solomon)
Bethlehem (David's birthplace)
Jerusalem (temple, seat of government)

OUTLINE—KING SOLOMON

1. Great king
2. Very prosperous
3. Son of David and Bathsheba
4. Friends with Hiram, king of Tyre, who sent materials to Jerusalem
5. Asked God for wisdom
6. Took 7 1/2 years to build the temple
7. Laid heavy taxes on the people
8. Married many strange women
9. Built altars to strange gods (1 Kings 11)
10. Had 700 wives and 300 concubines
11. Wrote 3000 proverbs and 1005 songs (1 Kings 4:32)
12. Solomon's provisions (1 Kings 4:22-30)
13. Wrote Song of Solomon, Proverbs, and Ecclesiastes

SHORT ANSWER QUESTIONS

1. The United Kingdom lasted for _____ years.

2. The three kings of the United Kingdom were _____,
_____, and _____.

3. Each reigned for _____ years.

4. _____, father of David.

5. _____, mother of Solomon.

6. _____, David's son who rebelled against him.

7, _____, Jonathan's lame son.

8. _____, captain of David's army.

9. _____, man who was killed because he touched
the ark.

10. _____, how many wives Solomon had.

11. What was Solomon's downfall? _____
_____

12. David's two punishments for his sins were _____
_____ and _____
_____.

13. _____ killed Absalom.

14. Name four of David's wives: _____, _____,
_____, and _____.

15. Absalom came home after being away from David for ____ years.

16. _____ raped Tamar, Absalom's sister.

17. _____, Bathsheba's first husband.

18. Solomon asked God for _____ when given a choice by God.

19. Solomon took ____ years to build the temple for God.

20. When the Queen of Sheba visited Solomon, she exclaimed, "_____."

THOUGHT QUESTIONS

1. Solomon was a king of wisdom, power, wealth and faith. How were strange women able to lead his heart away from God and cause him to build altars to strange gods? Does this indicate that women can have a tremendous power over the lives of men? What implications does this have for Christian women?

2. David loved and cared for his children and yet he had great difficulty with them. What characteristics did David have that would make him a good parent? What weaknesses and strengths of David are manifested in his children?

SPECIAL CHALLENGES

1. Do a special research project on the life of David or the life of Solomon. Use reference materials found in the church library or a home library.
2. Draw a diagram or make a model of the temple.
3. Conduct a special study of the book of Ecclesiastes or the Song of Solomon.
4. Study the Psalms that relate to different periods in David's life.
5. Be able to identify the characters in this study.
6. Be able to describe the events listed in the stories under "Suggested Stories To Note."
7. David cried out to God in his distress. Write a Psalm of thanksgiving to God for your blessings.
8. Be able to identify the following characters:

Joab	Uzzah
Amnon	Nathan
Absalom	Bathsheba
Solomon	Uriah
Tamar	

APPLICATION (2 Samuel 12:13; 24:10)

David sinned in many ways but he was willing to admit his mistakes and say, "I have sinned." Then he tried to recover from the sin and make things right with God. Think about these stories and answer the following questions:

- Do I try to hide my mistakes from God and my family?
- Do I blame someone else for my errors?
- Do I openly admit that I was wrong when someone calls my mistake to my attention?
- Why is it so hard for me to admit my sins?
- When someone points out a fault to me, do I apologize even

though I feel I was not the one in the wrong or do I argue my side?

• When I make mistakes, am I able to put them behind me and go on with my life?

SUGGESTIONS FOR TEACHING

Spend time in review. Review becomes more important as the class moves along with this narrative.

Sharing: David's children had great difficulty getting along with one another. Suggest how we can help siblings love one another and be kind to one another.

Prayer: Make a list of prayer requests and thanksgivings.

Options: 1. Review fact sheet, answer questions and talk about application.
2. Teacher or students tell the stories under "Suggested Stories To Note." Make application to our lives.
3. Have students report on the characters and make application.
4. Encourage those who accepted the challenges to share them with the class.
5. Encourage the reading of 2 Samuel and 1 Kings 1–11 outside of class and sharing thoughts with the class.
6. Role play suggested stories under the challenge.
7. For those interested in learning the characters in this material, make character cards or flash cards and drill on them in class. Each student may want to make his own set of cards.

Chapter Eight

The Divided Kingdom: Israel

1 KINGS 11–1 KINGS 17
ISRAEL—THE DOWNFALL OF A
MIGHTY NATION

When Solomon's son, Rehoboam, becomes king, ten tribes led by Jeroboam revolt against him. Thus, the divided kingdom begins. Ten tribes to the north become known as Israel. Israel's heart was not right with God, and the country didn't have one king who would tear down the idols that King Jeroboam had set up. Stories of people and places—faithfulness and unfaithfulness—prevail in these accounts.

- **God Takes the Kingdom Away from Solomon**
  Before Solomon died, God told him that He would take the kingdom away from him because of his sins and give it to a servant (I Kings 11:11)

- **Rehoboam, Solomon's son, Becomes King (1 Kings 12)**

- **Ten Tribes Revolt Against Rehoboam (1 Kings 12)**
  The tribes wanted their burdens made lighter and Rehoboam refused. The tribes were led by a dynamic leader, Jeroboam (a former servant of Solomon.)

- **Ten Tribes Form a New Kingdom (1 Kings 12)**
  The ten tribes were a northern kingdom and were called Israel. Jeroboam was their new king. Because he was afraid the people would go to Jerusalem for worship and turn back to Rehoboam, he immediately set up two calves for them to worship, one at Dan and one at Bethel. These calves remained in Israel and were a snare unto the people.

FACTS ABOUT ISRAEL

- Composed of 10 tribes
- Made Jeroboam the first king
- Had 9 different dynasties
- Had 19 kings
- Lasted 250 years
- Taken into captivity by the Assyrians (2 Kings 17)
- Had no good kings although some were better than others
- Had a capital built in Samaria

PROPHETS TO ISRAEL

Elijah
Elisha
Amos
Jonah   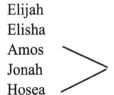   prophesied during the reign of Jeroboam II
Hosea

Kings of Israel	Reign	Prophets
Jeroboam	22 years	
Nadab	2 years	
Baasha	24 years	
Elah	2 years	
Zimri	7 days	
Omri	12 years	
Ahab	22 years	Elijah
Ahaziah	2 years	
Jehoram	12 years	Elisha
Jehu	28 years	
Jehoahaz	17 years	
Joash (Jehoash)	16 years	
Jeroboam II	41 years	Jonah, Amos, Hosea
Zachariah	6 months	Jonah, Amos, Hosea
Shallum	1 month	Jonah, Amos, Hosea
Menahem	10 years	
Pekahiah	2 years	
Pekah	20 years	
Hoshea	9 years	

OUTLINE OF THE KINGS OF ISRAEL

*I.   **Jeroboam** (22 years)
    A. Leader of rebellion
    B. Set up idols at Dan and Bethel
    C. Appointed priests of the lowest of the people
    D. Man of God prophesied against him and his hand withered
    E. Sent wife to prophet when his son, Abijah, fell sick; son died
    F. Fought with Abijam, king of Judah, and was defeated
    G. Known in the Bible as "the man who made Israel to sin"

II. **Nadab** (2 years)
    A. Son of Jeroboam
    B. Did evil
    C. Was killed by Baasha

*III. **Baasha** (24 years)
    A. Of the house of Issachar
    B. Slew all the house of Jeroboam
    C. War between Asa, king of Judah, and Baasha
    D. Did evil in the sight of the Lord

IV. **Elah** (2 years)
    A. Was killed by Zimri when he was drunken

*V. **Zimri** (7 days)
    A. Put to death all the house of Baasha
    B. Set the palace on fire during a siege and killed himself
    C. Omri, captain of the host, was made king by the people

*VI. **Omri** (12 years)
    A. Bought a hill and built the city of Samaria on it
    B. Did worse than all before him

VII. **Ahab** (22 years)
    A. Son of Omri
    B. Did worse than all before him
    C. Married Jezebel, daughter of the king of Zidonians
    D. Worshipped and served Baal—made groves and altars
    E. Elijah prophesied against him
    F. Contest on Mt. Carmel between the prophets of Baal and Elijah
    G. Jezebel gets Naboth's vineyard
    H. Fought 3 battles with the Syrians
        1. Won the first two battles
        2. United with Jehoshaphat, king of Judah, in the third battle, was killed by the Syrians

    I.   Humbled himself in his last days

    J.   Prophesied that the kingdom would be taken away and the dogs would eat his remains

XIII.   **Ahaziab** (2 years)

    A. Son of Ahab

    B. Walked in the way of his father and mother

    C. Fell through a lattice in an upper chamber and injured himself

    D. Sent to inquire of God of Ekron if he would get well

    E. Messengers met Elijah; messengers die; Elijah goes to Ahaziah and tells him he will die

IX.   **Jehoram** (12 years)

    A. Son of Ahab because Ahaziah had no sons

    B. Did evil, but not like Ahab; put away Baal

    C. United with Jehosaphat against Moab. Defeated Moab by the hand of God; saw water in ditches and thought it was blood

    D. Syrians were led into the city of Samaria by Elisha

    E. A year later, Samaria was beseiged by Benhadad, king of Syria, and a great famine prevailed; people ate their children

    F   Israel went into the camp of Syrians and took their spoil

    G. United with Ahaziah, king of Judah, against Syria

    H. Was wounded in the battle with Syria, and was later killed by Jehu

X.   **Jehu** (28 years)

    A. Destroyed Jehoram and all the house of Ahab

    B. Drove his chariot furiously

    C. Destroyed Baal worship but not the calves at Dan and Bethel

    D. Four generations would sit on the throne because he obeyed God

      E.   Invaded by Hazael and the Syrians who took the territory east of the Jordan

XI.   **Jehoahaz** (17 years)
- A. Son of Jehu
- B. Did evil and the people were delivered into the hand of the Syrians

XII.   **Joash** (Jehoash) (16 years)
- A. Son of Johoahaz
- B. Did evil
- C. Elisha is sick, Joash weeps over him; Elisha dies
- D. Fought with the Syrians and took the cities they had taken away (smites them three times)
- E. Fought with Amaziah, king of Judah, and defeated them

XIII.   **Jeroboam II** (41 years)
- A. Son of Joash
- B. Took back the territory that the Syrians had taken
- C. Reigned during a prosperous time in Israel
- D. Jonah, Hosea, and Amos prophesied during his reign

XIV.   **Zachariah** (6 months)
- A. Son of Jeroboam
- B. Was slain by Shallum
- C. Did evil

*XV.   **Shallum** (1 month)
- A. Was slain by Menahem
- B. Did evil

*XVI. **Menahem** (10 years)
- A. Was very wicked
- B. Took the city of Tiphash and slew the pregnant women
- C. Paid tribute to Pul, king of Assyria

XVII.   **Pekahiah** (2 years)
     A.   Son of Menahem
     B.   Did evil
     C.   Was slain by Pekah

*XVIII. **Pekah** (22 years)
     A.   Did evil
     B.   Tiglath-pileser invaded the country and took captives to Assyria
     C.   Killed by Hoshea

*XIX.   **Hoshea** (9 years)
     A.   Did evil but not like the kings before him
     B.   Shalmaneser, king of Assyria, came against Israel and took them
     C.   Samaria was besieged for 3 years
     D.   Hoshea refused to pay tribute to Assyria and sent for help from So, king of Egypt.
     E.   Ten tribes are deported to Assyria, never to rise again

*dynasties

SUGGESTED SCRIPTURES TO NOTE

1 Kings
Division of the kingdom (12)
Sins of Israel (14:16, 23; 15:34)
Sins of Omri's family (16:25, 26,30-33)
Elijah and the widow (17)
Contest on Mt. Carmel (18:1740)
Jezebel's wickedness (19:1-3)
Elijah's faithfulness (9:18)
Naboth's vineyard (21)
Death of Ahab (22:34-40)

2 Kings
   God chooses Elisha (2)
   Shunammite woman and Elisha (4)
   Naaman's cleansing (5)
   Death of Jezebel (9:3-37)
   Sins continue (10:29)
   Captivity by the Assyrians (17)

CHARACTER LIST

Jeroboam	Rehoboam	Elijah
Elisha	Ahab	Jezebel
Naboth	Jehu	Shunammite woman
Naaman	Amos	Jonah
Hosea		

PROPHETS TO ISRAEL

- Amos prophesied during the reign of Jeroboam II. He was a country preacher from the hills of Tekoa in Judah who went to Israel to preach to them. He warned them about neglect, moral corruption and spiritual pride. He prophesied of the captivity to come if they refused to obey God. Interesting passages to note are: 2:6; 3:7, 12-15; 4:12; 5:21-27; 6:4-6; 7:8, 10-17; 8:2; 9:14, 15

- Jonah prophesied during the reign of Jeroboam II. Most of us remember the story of Jonah and the whale. Jonah didn't want to preach to the people of Nineveh (capital of Assyria) because they were the enemies of Israel. God taught him a lesson. In 2 Kings 14:25, the Bible says Jonah was a spokesman for God to the people of Israel.

- Hosea also prophesied during the reign of Jeroboam II. Some scholars think this book is an allegory while others feel the story actually took place. In the story God tells Hosea to marry a harlot. He marries Gomer and she bears him three children: Jezreel, Loruhamah, and Loammi. Her leaving him brings great heartache to him. Hosea buys her back. God is teaching Hosea a lesson about His relationship with the children of Israel. Hosea preaches about the sins of Israel.

MAP SEARCH

Samaria	Mt. Carmel
Dan	Assyria
Bethel	

Use map on pages 74 and 112.

SHORT ANSWER QUESTIONS

1. The three kings of the United Kingdom were _____, _____, and _____.

2. Solomon sinned by

3. _____ was Solomon's son who became king.

4. _____ (number) tribes revolted about the king's decision to make their burdens harder.

5. The leader of the revolt was _____ who later became king.

6. Jeroboam set up idols at _____ and
    _____.

7. Israel lasted for _____ years.

8. Israel had _____ number of kings.

9. Israel was carried captive by the _____

10. Two prophets to Israel who did not write a book were
    _____ and _____.

11. _____, _____, and
    _____ were writing prophets to Israel.

12. _____ and his wife _____ were
    the most wicked leaders of Israel.

13. Ahab and Jezebel stole _____ vineyard.

14. _____, a Syrian, was cleansed of his leprosy by
    the power of God through Elijah.

15. _____ was chosen to succeed Elijah.

16. The contest on Mt. Carmel was between _____
    and _____.

17. How did Elisha help the Shunammite woman and how did she
    help him?_____
    _____
    _____

THOUGHT QUESTIONS

1. Elijah was discouraged after the contest on Mt. Carmel when Jezebel was seeking his life. (1 Kings 19) What did Elijah do to overcome his discouragement? What circumstances make us discouraged today and what can we do to overcome discouragement?

2. In the story of Hosea and Gomer, God wanted Hosea to have an object lesson in pain, hurt and disappointment. Is it necessary for us to experience some of these things before we can teach others about them? What about sin? Is it necessary to experience drunkenness, adultery, unfaithfulness, and so on, before one can teach about it?

SPECIAL CHALLENGES

1. Get together with a friend this week and study this material. Generally, this period in the Jews' history is unknown to church members. It helps when you review with a friend.
2. Be able to recite the facts about Israel and identify the character list and prophets to Israel.
3. Memorize the kings of Israel, in order.*
4. Read 1 and 2 Kings. Especially note "Suggested Scriptures to Note."

*Ambitious students only

APPLICATION (Amos)

The children of Israel lived in very prosperous times during the day of Amos. They had summer houses and winter houses; they had beds of ivory and ate tender steaks. (3:15; 6:4) They were going to worship but were not living godly lives. They had forgotten the poor, had moral corruption and had a spiritual pride that was not good. God said He hated their worship. (5:21-23)

Does the time of Amos sound like our time today? We live in very affluent times. We go to worship but do we have our heart in it? Have we forgotten others who are less fortunate than we? What have we done this week to show others that we care about them? We usually turn to God in time of trouble. What can we do to improve our relationship with God during good times?

SUGGESTIONS FOR TEACHING

Sharing: The Shunammite woman showed hospitality to Elisha. Tell the class about a time when you showed hospitality and you felt good about it.

Prayer: Make a list of prayer requests and thanksgivings.

Options: 1.   Be sure everyone understands what happened at the end of Solomon's reign. It is better to spend class time on the overall picture and let students read the narrative stories on their own. Our purpose is to build a frame for further Bible study.
2.   Teacher or student tells the stories under "Suggested Stories to Note" Make application to our lives.
3.   Review, Drill, Review*
4.   Divide into two groups and let class members recite the facts to each other. Reciting helps us to remember.

*Don't apologize for review. Review is one of the principles of learning.

The Northern Kingdom

Solomon's sins were the catalyst for
A kingdom divided and internal war.
His son, Rehoboam, was next in line
To rule the United Kingdom, but then we find.

Ten tribes revolt and with Jeroboam they side.
And to the north they choose to go and reside.
Israel is the name of the Northern Kingdom, now new
And the worship of idols became their purview.

When the good people and the Levites learned this was Israel's ways,
Back to Judah they went for the rest of their days.
The kings were all bad—not one was found good
Nineteen rulers from nine dynasties did all the wicked they could.

After living in sin for 250 years,
The world power of Assyria came and stirred up some fears.
They took Israel captive and scattered them around
Until a full-blooded Israelite was not to be found.

—Faye Gibson

The Kingdoms of Israel and Judah

Chapter Nine

The Divided Kingdom: Judah

1 KINGS (11–22) — 2 KINGS
2 CHRONICLES 10–36
(Chronicles gives a more complete account of Judah)

JUDAH—A KINGDOM THAT TURNS AWAY FROM DAVID, ITS FATHER

Judah, the southern kingdom, was comprised of two tribes and existed for 350 years before being taken into captivity by the Babylonians. There were great kings such as Hezekiah and Josiah who led the people back to God and there were also very wicked kings. The stories of Judah are filled with excitement, joy, God's anger, God's glory, obedience and disobedience. One is made aware of the need to serve and obey God from reading these accounts.

- **God Takes the Kingdom Away From Solomon**
  Before Solomon died, God told him that He would take the kingdom away from him because of his sins and give it to a servant
  (1 Kings 11:1)

- **Rehoboam, Solomon's son, becomes king (1 Kings 12)**

- **Two Tribes Remain with Rehoboam (1 Kings 12:21)**
  Judah
  Benjamin
  (In Time—The Levites came to Judah)

- **Advantages of Judah Over Israel**
  Judah was the stronger kingdom
  All the kings were in the lineage of David
  Jerusalem and the temple were located in Jerusalem
  The Levites, the priestly tribe, remained with Judah
  The people who wanted to serve God came to Judah
      (2 Chronicles 11:16)
  Judah had several good kings who led the people back to God

- **Facts About Judah**
  Comprised of two tribes, Judah and Benjamin
  Made Rehoboam, Solomon's son, the first king
  Had one dynasty, all in the family of David
  Had 19 kings and one queen
  Lasted 350 years (100 years more than Israel)
  Taken into captivity by the Babylonians
  Continued to maintain the temple and the seat of government at
      Jerusalem
  Had several good kings, namely Asa, Jehoshaphat, Hezekiah and
      Josiah.

Prophets to Judah
- Isaiah—Prophesied in the days of Uzziah, Jotham and
  Hezekiah

- Micah—Prophesied in the days of Jotham, Ahaz and Hezekiah
- Joel—It is believed that he prophesied in the early years of King Joash
- Nahum—Prophesied about the fall of Nineveh
- Habbakuk—The theme of his prophesy is the Chaldean invasion
- Zephaniah—Prophesied in the days of Josiah
- Jeremiah—Prophesied on the eve of the Babylonian captivity by giving information regarding himself and the events that happened during his ministry. He warned the people about their sins. It is thought that he wrote the book of Lamentations.
- Obadiah—It is believed that he prophesied shortly after the destruction of Jerusalem by Nebuchadnezzar
- Daniel & Ezekiel—Prophesied in Babylonian captivity
- Haggai, Zechariah and Malachi—Prophesied after the return from Babylonian captivity

JUDAH

Kings	Reign	Prophets
Rehoboam	17 years	
Abijah	3 years	
Asa**	41 years	
Jehoshaphat**	25 years	
Jehoram	8 years	
Ahaziah	1 year	
Athaliah (queen)	6 years	
Joash*	42 years	Joel
Amaziah*	29 years	
Uzziah**	52 years	Isaiah
Jotham**	16 years	Micah
Ahaz	16 years	
Hezekiah**	29 years	

Manasseh	55 years	
Amon	2 years	Nahum
Josiah**	31 years	Zephaniah
Jehoahaz	3 months	Jeremiah
Jehoiakim	11 years	Habakkuk
Jehoiachin	3 months	Daniel
Zedekiah	11 years	Ezekiel

**Good
*Mostly Good

KINGDOM OF JUDAH
KINGS AND THEIR REIGNS

I.   **Rehoboam** (17 year reign)
    A. Son of Solomon
    B. Did evil and 10 tribes revolted against him
    C. Forsook God and all Israel with him
    D. Shishak, king of Egypt, came against Judah and took to Egypt the treasures of the temple and the king's house

II.   **Abijah or Abijam** (3 year reign)
    A. Fought with Israel
    B. Made a speech to Israel and then defeated them

III.   **Asa** (41 year reign)

    A. Did that which is good and right
    B. Took away idols and high places (some remained)
    C. Smote Ethiopians
    D. Made an alliance with Syria against Israel, which displeased God
    E. Put Hanani, the seer, in prison when he condemned him
    F. Had disease in his feet and sought physicians instead of God

IV.   **Jehoshaphat** (25 year reign)

    A. Had riches and honor, was great king (greatest since Solomon) 2 Chronicles 17:3-5
    B. Sent Levites throughout the land to teach the people
    C. Kingdoms around him feared him and paid tribute to him
    D. Made an alliance with King Ahab
    E. Moab and Ammon came against him and God helps Judah
    F. Joins with Ahaziah to send ships to Tarshish, God is displeased and ships are broken

V.   **Jehoram** (8 year reign)
    A. Killed all his brethren, married Athaliah, daughter of Ahab and Jezebel
    B. Did evil in the sight of God
    C. A revolt of the Edomites and Libnah came to Jerusalem and took everything in Jehoram's house, except for Jehoahaz, his son
    D. Had incurable disease as prophesied by Elijah
    E. Was not buried in the sepulcher of his fathers

VI.   **Ahaziah or Jehoahaz** (1 year reign)
    A. Counseled by his mother, Athaliah
    B. Was very wicked
    C. Formed alliance with Jehoram, king of Israel and was killed by Jehu

VII. **Athaliah** (6 year reign)
    A. Daughter of Ahab and Jezebel
    B. Slew all of the royal house except Joash, who was hidden by a nurse for six years in the temple
    C. Was killed

VIII. **Joash** (42 year reign) *king at age 7*
    A. Jehoida, the priest, brought Joash out and made him king at age seven
    B. Jehoida guided him well, and Joash did right all the days of Jehoida
    C. Broke down idols, established temple worship, repaired

and refurnished the temple
   D. Jehoida died and was buried among the kings
   E. After the priest's death, idol worship was restored
   F. Judah, because of their sins, was defeated by the Syrians
   G. Joash was slain by his servants while in bed
IX. **Amaziah** (29 year reign)
   A. Slew all the servants who had killed his father
   B. Battled with Edom, won the battle, but carried their gods back to Judah and worshipped them
   C. Fought Israel but was defeated
   D. Was killed
X. **Uzziah** (52 year reign)
   A. Became king at age 16
   B. Did that which was right all the days of Zechariah, the priest
   C. Conquered nations about him—a time of prosperity equal with that of Solomon's time
   D. Went into temple and offered incense—was stricken with leprosy
 XI. **Jotham** (16 year reign)
   A. Was upright, but the people were corrupt
   B. Strengthened defenses and built cities
XII. **Ahaz** (16 year reign)
   A. Did evil, worshipped Baal
   B. Was defeated by the Syrians, Israel, Edom and the Philistines
   C. Appealed to Assyria for help
   D. Was not buried in the sepulcher of the kings
XIII. **Hezekiah** (29 year reign)
   A. Did that which was good and right
   B. Commanded the people to obey God, destroyed idols
   C. Invaded by the Assyrians, saved by God—185,000 Assyrian soldiers died
   D. God adds 15 years to his life—gave sundial as a sign
   E. Showed his wealth to Babylon—a mistake

      F. Buried in chiefest of sepulchers of sons of David

XIV.   **Manasseh** (55 year reign)

      A. Twelve years old when he began to reign

      B. Reinstated Baal worship

      C. Assyria came against him, carried him captive to Babylon, called upon the Lord, was restored to his throne

      D. Manasseh returns to the Lord

      E. Was buried in the garden of his own house

XV.   **Amon** (2 year reign)

      A. Very wicked

      B. Was killed by his own people

XVI.   **Josiah** (31 year reign)

      A. Eight years old when he began to reign

      B. Did that which was right and good

      C. Destroyed worship of Baal, repaired the temple, found the book of Moses

      D. Necho, king of Egypt, came against him; Josiah was wounded

      E. Buried with honor

XVII. **Jehoahaz** (3 month reign)

      A. Did evil

      B. Necho took to Egypt where he died

XVIII. **Jehoiakim** (11 year reign)

      A. Placed on the throne by Pharaoh Necho

      B. Name was changed from Eliakim to Jehoiakim

      C. Paid tribute to the king of Egypt, became tributary to king of Babylon. After three years he rebelled

      D. Several nations came against him

      E. Nebuchadnezzar carried him to Babylon where he died

XIX.   **Jehoiachin** (3 month reign)

      A. Very wicked

      B. Nebuchadnezzar took Jerusalem and took the king captive

XX.   **Zedekiah** (11 year reign)

      A. Placed on throne by King Nebuchadnezzar

      B. Rebelled against Babylon

          C. Babylon besieged Jerusalem for more than a year and carried the Jews to Babylon

          D. Zedekiah's sons were killed, and his eyes were put out

XXI. **Judah After the Fall**

          A. Gedaliah was made governor

          B. A poor remnant was left

          C. Jeremiah stayed with this group

          D. Gedaliah was murdered by treachery from within

          E. People fled to Egypt against the warning of Jeremiah

SUGGESTED STORIES TO NOTE

- The Foolishness of Rehoboam (2 Chronicles 10)
- Jehoshaphat, A Good King (2 Chronicles 17:1-6)
- Jehoshaphat and Ahab United in Battle (2 Chronicles 18)
- Jehoram, Jehoshaphat's Son, Marries Ahab's Daughter, Athaliah (2 Chronicles 21:1-6)
- Athaliah's Wickedness, Becomes Queen (2 Chronicles 22, 23)
- Hezekiah Invites Israel to the Passover (2 Chronicles 30)
- King of Assyria Comes Against Hezekiah (2 Kings 19, 2 Chronicles 32:1-23)
- Hezekiah's Life is Extended Fifteen Years (2 Kings 20:1-11)
- Josiah Leads the People Back to God (2 Chronicles 34, 35)
- Nebuchadnezzar Takes Babylon (2 Chronicles 36, 2 Kings 25)

CHARACTER LIST
(Main characters only)

Rehoboam	Jehoshaphat	Jehoram
Athaliah	Hezekiah	Josiah
Isaiah	Nebuchadnezzar	Isaiah
Jeremiah		

MAP SEARCH

Judah (tribe)   .   Benjamin (tribe)
Jerusalem   Babylon

SHORT ANSWER QUESTIONS

1. We read about Judah in the books of _____,
   _____, and _____

2. Two tribes, _____ and _____
   made up the kingdom of Judah.

3. _____ was an educated prophet who prophesied
   during the days of Hezekiah.

4. _____ prophesied on the eve of the captivity,
   warning the people of their sins.

5. All the kings of Judah were in the family of _____

6. Judah lasted _____ years before they were taken into captivity.

7. _____, _____, and
   _____ were three good kings of Judah.

8. Rehoboam listened to _____ regarding
   the burdens of the people.

9. Jehoshaphat united with _____ in battle.

10. Jehoshaphat's son, _____, married Ahab
    and Jezebel's daughter named _____.

11. When Assyria came against Hezekiah, he turned to
    _____.

12. Name two ways Athaliah was wicked: _____
    _____.

13. Hezekiah's life was extended by _____ years
    because of his prayer. God gave him the sign of
    _____.

14. One of the good deeds of Josiah was to _____.

15. _____, king of Babylon, captured
    Judah.

THOUGHT QUESTIONS

1. Jeremiah cried as he begged the people to turn to God. He
   warned of destruction and captivity, and yet they gave no heed.
   Why wouldn't these people listen to Jeremiah? What causes a
   people to get so far away from God that they refuse to listen?
   What are the dangers of this happening in our time?

2. Athaliah was a very wicked woman. She did evil, was a wicked
   wife, and counseled her son to do evil. Her son was very wicked
   also. Who do you think has the strongest influence on a child: a
   good mother or an evil one? How much influence can a godly
   mother have on a child? Sometimes children of Christian parents just develop the faith of their parents. What can we do to
   help our children develop their own personal faith?

SPECIAL CHALLENGES

1. Get together with a friend this week and study this material. Generally, this period in the Jews' history is unknown to church members. It helps when you review with a friend.
2. Be able to recite the facts about Judah and identify the character list and prophets to Judah.
3. Memorize the kings of Judah, in order. *
4. Read 1 and 2 Kings and 2 Chronicles. Especially note stories listed under "Suggested Stories to Note"

   *Ambitious students only

APPLICATION

Hezekiah was a great man of God as exhibited by the following incidents:

he tore down idols

he trusted in the Lord

he turned to God when Assyria came against him

he turned to God in time of sickness

he invited others to worship in Jerusalem

Make a specific list of examples in your life that would indicate great faith such as that of Hezekiah.

SUGGESTIONS FOR TEACHING

Sharing: Hezekiah and Josiah both proclaimed great revivals during their time. Tell about a time when you were a part of a great revival or tell what you think a revival should be. (2 Chronicles 30, 35)

Prayer:

Options: 1. Tell the story of Judah, stressing the highlights so students will see the overall picture.
2. Teacher or students tell the stories under "Suggested Stories to Note." Make application to our lives.

The Southern Kingdom

While Israel was the kingdom to the north,
Judah to the south was coming forth.
Two tribes there dwelled and twenty rulers did reign
Eight of them good and twelve were a pain!

Judah and Benjamin were the tribes who comprise
The kingdom of Judah plus those from Levi.
Though the people from God did eventually turn
Later some good kings caused Judah to discern.

That their fathers before them were leading them right
And God's ways were the cause for which they should fight.
All kings were from the family of David who was to be
The lineage from which Christ we would eventually see.

—Faye Gibson

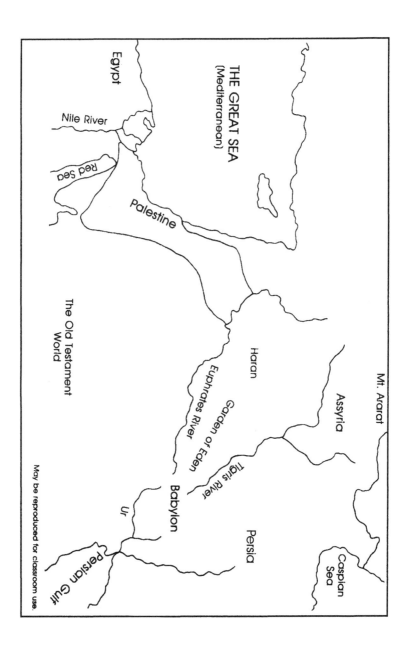

THE GREAT SEA
(Mediterranean)

Egypt

Nile River

Red Sea

Palestine

The Old Testament
World

Haran

Euphrates River

Garden of Eden

Tigris River

Babylon

Ur

Persia

Assyria

Mt. Ararat

Caspian
Sea

Persian Gulf

May be reproduced for classroom use.

Chapter Ten

The Babylonian Captivity

70 Years
DANIEL 1–6
THE BABYLONIAN CAPTIVITY

King Nebuchadnezzar led a siege against Judah and was victorious. The people who were physically able to make the trip were taken to Babylon. There they lived for seventy years. Daniel records the events of this captivity. Once again we see the power of God and His protecting hand.

FACT SHEET ON THE BABYLONIAN CAPTIVITY

The Carrying Away into Babylon by King Nebuchadnezzar
1. Under Jehoiakim
   a. Carried vessels of the temple
   b. Daniel, Shadrach, Meshach, and Abednego

2. Under Jehoiachin
    a. Carried all Jerusalem, 10,000 captives
    b. Left poorest sort of people behind
3. Under Zedekiah
    a. Final deportation
    b. Left only a small remnant for Gedaliah

The Captivity: They lived as colonists, built houses, planted gardens, took wives, and begat children. They were forbidden to offer sacrifices but were permitted to assemble in public worship on the sabbath and to read scriptures. Some of them such as Daniel rose to positions of honor. The captivity lasted 70 years. Daniel and Ezekiel prophesied during the captivity.

BOOK OF DANIEL (Chapters 1–6)

Chapter 1
  A. Nebuchadnezzar besieges Jerusalem
  B. Daniel, Shadrach, Meshach, and Abednego are taken to Babylon
  C. Daniel refuses to eat the king's meat
Chapter 2
  A. King Nebuchadnezzar dreams about a great image
  B. Daniel interprets the dream
  C. The image is a prophecy concerning the coming of the church
  D. Daniel is made a ruler in Babylon
Chapter 3
  A. King Nebuchadnezzar makes a large image of gold
  B. Shadrach, Meshach, and Abednego refuse to worship the image
  C. The boys are put in a fiery furnace, but God protects them
  D. Nebuchadnezzar blesses Jehovah God

Chapter 4

    A. King Nebuchadnezzar dreams about a tree growing and then being cut down

    B. Daniel interprets the dream

    C. The dream means Nebuchadnezzar would be driven from men and act as an animal and then be restored

    D. The dream is fulfilled

Chapter 5

    A Belshazzar, Nebuchadnezzar's grandson, was proclaimed king

    B. Belshazzar made a great feast

    C. The nobles drank wine from the vessels that were taken from the temple in Jerusalem

    D. A man's fingers wrote on the wall

    E. The writing was: MENE, MENE, TEKEL, UPHARSIN

    F. The writing meant the kingdom would be taken away from Babylon and given to the Medes and the Persians

    G. The Medes and the Persians take over

Chapter 6

    A Darius is made king and makes Daniel one of three presidents

    B. The noblemen conspire against Daniel and have a decree made that no one can pray to any god except the king

    C. Daniel continues to face Jerusalem and pray three times a day

    D. Daniel is put in the lions' den, but God protects him

    E. Daniel prospers in the reign of Darius and Cyrus

CHARACTER LIST

King Nebuchadnezzar	Shadrach
Daniel	Meshach
Ezekiel	Abednego
King Belshazzar	King Darius
King Cyrus	

MAP SEARCH

Locate Babylon, Persia, and Media on a map. Using a map scale of miles, determine how far the journey was from Jerusalem to Babylon.

SHORT ANSWER QUESTIONS

1. When King _____ destroyed Jerusalem, he carried four young men, _____, _____, _____, and _____ back with him to Babylon.

2. He also took the _____ of the temple back to Babylon.

3. The two prophets during the captivity were _____ and _____.

4. King Nebuchadnezzar's grandson, _____, became king after Nebuchadnezzar.

5. The writing on the wall was _____.

6. The writing on the wall meant _____ _____.

7. The _____ and _____ took over the _____ empire.

THOUGHT QUESTIONS

1. In the Old Testament God allowed sinful nations to be overtaken and destroyed. Does God still act in this way today? Would America be classified as a sinful nation?

2. King Nebuchadnezzar was a very powerful man. God brought him down to a state where he acted like an animal. He was humbled. Does God still do this today? Can you think of powerful people who have been humbled?

APPLICATION

Daniel refused to eat the king's meat even though his refusal might bring him great harm. Shadrach, Meshach, and Abednego refused to bow down to a graven image even though their refusal would cause them to be put in a fiery furnace. Daniel continued to pray even though his doing so caused him to be put in a den of lions. Have you ever obeyed God under adverse circumstances? Think of examples of people (especially missionaries) who have put their lives in jeopardy by serving the Lord. Will these who have given so much have a greater reward? What have you given up for the Lord? What are you willing to give up for the Lord? House? Money? Time? Power? Energy?

SPECIAL CHALLENGES

1. Draw the image in Nebuchadnezzar's dream. Label all the parts and give the interpretation of the dream.
2. Read Daniel 1–6
3. Be able to identify the characters in the story.
4. Write a song about one of the characters in this lesson. Write it to the tune of "Row, Row, Row Your Boat."
5. Design a bumper sticker that teaches us to keep doing good in spite of adversities.

SUGGESTIONS FOR TEACHING

Sharing: Daniel refused to eat meat and ate vegetables. Let each share a favorite vegetable.

Prayer: Prayer requests

Options: 1. Have someone tell the following stories
   A.   Daniel refuses to eat the king's meat
   B.   The image of Nebuchadnezzar's dream
   C.   The three boys refuse to bow down to the image
   D.   Nebuchadnezzar's dream about the tree
   E.   The handwriting on the wall

2. Have someone assigned to do research on how the Medes and Persians took over the Babylonian empire and report it to the class.

3. Make flashcards and review characters.

4. Encourage the reading of Daniel 1–6 and have a discussion about the reading.

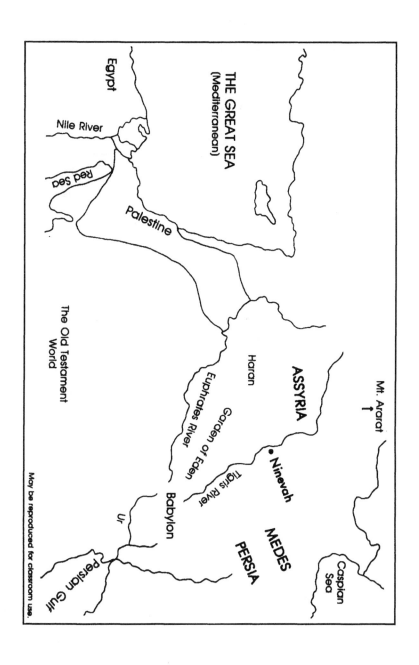

Chapter Eleven

Return From Babylonian Captivity

Ezra–Nehemiah
FACT SHEET ON THE RETURN
FROM BABYLONIAN CAPTIVITY

Isaiah (Isaiah 44:28) prophesied 160 years before it happened that King Cyrus, King of Persia, would come to power and free the Jews. We read of this decree from Cyrus in Ezra 1. King Cyrus charged the Jews to go home to Jerusalem. There were three men who led a group back to Jerusalem.

BOOK OF EZRA

I.   Return under Zerubbabel
      A. Decree of Cyrus
      B. 49,897 common people, priests and Levites returned

  C. Built an altar in Jerusalem

  D. Foundation of temple was laid

  E. The help of the Samaritans offered and refused

  F. Decree of Artaxerxes, received letters from Samaritans, said the work should stop

  G. Haggai and Zachariah encouraged the people to work again

  H. Cyrus' decree confirmed by Darius

  I. Temple was completed under the leadership of Zerubbabel, had dedicatory service

II. Esther becomes queen of Persia.

III. Return under Ezra (Ezra)

  A. 7th year of Artaxerxes

  B. Proclaimed a fast for God to help them on their journey

  C. Princes complained that the people had intermarried with people of the land

  D. Ezra rent his clothes, the people confessed their sins

  E. Required people to give up strange (foreign) wives

IV. Return under Nehemiah (20th year of Artaxerxes)

  A. Nehemiah hears news of the affliction of the children of Israel

  B. King sends Nehemiah to Jerusalem

  C. He goes by night to view the ruined walls in Jerusalem

  D. Began rebuilding walls

  E. Enemies oppose rebuilding: Sanballat, Tobiah, Geshem

  F. Nehemiah sets watch, lives as common people.

  G. Walls are completed in 52 days

  H. Census taken

  I. Law read and explained. People fast, repent and confess

  J. Nehemiah tries to encourage keeping of Sabbath

  K. Nehemiah rebukes intermarriage

THREE WRITING PROPHETS

There were three prophets who prophesied to the Jews when they returned to Jerusalem—Haggai, Zechariah, and Malachi (the last three books of the Old Testament).

CLOSE OF THE OLD TESTAMENT

The Old Testament closes with the rebuilding of the walls and the temple in Jerusalem. The people were looking for a prophet, a Messiah, as prophesied in the books of Zechariah and Malachi.

CHARACTER LIST

King Cyrus	Artaxerxes	Malachi
Zerubbabel	Darius	Sanballat
Ezra	Haggai	Tobiah
Nehemiah	Zechariah	Geshem

MAP SEARCH

Show the journey from Babylon to Jerusalem on a map. Point out where the Samaritans lived.

SHORT ANSWER QUESTIONS

1. We read of the return to Jerusalem in the books of _____
    and _____.

2. King _____, king of _____,
    freed the Jews and allowed them to return to their land.

3. Three men led a group back: _____,
    _____, and _____.

4. They rebuilt the _____ and the _____.

5. Three prophets after the return were _____,
    _____, and _____.

6. Three men who tried to stop the building in Jerusalem were
    _____, _____, and
    _____.

THOUGHT QUESTIONS

1. The men in Ezra's day were required to put away the strange wives they had taken (Ezra 10). What was involved in this separation? What about children? Are we sometimes required to do difficult things to show our commitment to God?

2. Nehemiah longed to go home to Jerusalem and help his people rebuild their city. What do you long to do for the Lord? What can you do for the Lord?

3. When the walls of Jerusalem were built, families worked together to build a section of the wall (Nehemiah 3). Shallum (Nehemiah 3:12) apparently had no sons and he had his daughters help him in this undertaking. What spiritual activities can families engage in today? Do youth programs encourage or discourage family activities? What can we do to encourage more family involvement in church activities?

SPECIAL CHALLENGES

1. Read the books of Ezra and Nehemiah, keeping the background of this material in mind.
2. Review the story of Judah in captivity.
3. Find all the Messianic passages in the books of Zechariah and Malachi and see how they are fulfilled in Christ.

APPLICATION (Nehemiah 4:6)

The people built the walls of Jerusalem because "they had a mind to work." They had a difficult task and met opposition, yet they continued to build. How many tasks do we complete because we have "a mind to work?" What characteristics help us complete difficult tasks in our lives? What happens when a negative force tries to keep us from reaching a goal? What is a personal goal that you have been unable to reach at the present time, and why are you not reaching it?

SUGGESTIONS FOR TEACHING

Sharing: Share an activity that your family enjoys doing together.

Prayer: Prayer requests

Options: 1.   Have someone share the stories of:
                     A.   Return under Zerubbabel
                     B.   Return under Ezra
                     C.   Return under Nehemiah
                     D.   The opposition of the Samaritans
              2.   Review characters, make flash cards
              3.   Encourage the reading of the books of Ezra and Nehemiah and sharing thoughts with the class.
              4.   Encourage those who accepted the challenges to share them with the class.

Chapter Twelve

Between the Testaments

BETWEEN THE TESTAMENTS

The Old Testament closes and God gives us 400 years of silence before we are given the New Testament. Many events, people and places change during this period. It is interesting to learn of these events from history to help us better understand the New Testament.

FACT SHEET

- There were 400 years between the Old Testament and the New Testament

- After the Persian empire collapsed, the Greeks were in power.

- Alexander the Great lived during the time of the Greeks' dominion.

- Following the Greek period, the Romans took power.

- When the New Testament opens, the Jews are under the dominion of Roman rule.

- During the intertestament period, the Greek language became the universal language, which paved the way for the Greek New Testament.

- The Romans built roads during the intertestament period which made possible the spread of Christianity.

- Synagogues became a place of worship. (Many think these were started in Babylon, but the Bible makes no mention of them.)

- Many religious groups arose during this time: Pharisees, Sadducees, Zealots, Scribes, Essenes, Herodians.

- The Sanhedrin became the Jewish court of law.

Research in a Bible Dictionary the following:

1. Sanhedrin
2. Pharisees
3. Sadducees
4. Zealots
5. Scribes
6. Essenes
7. Herodians

THOUGHT QUESTIONS

1. How did the events that occurred between the testaments aid in the spread of Christianity?

2. Why was God silent and not in communication with His people for 400 years?

APPLICATION

King Nebuchadnezzar, king of Babylon, was a powerful man who thought he could not be conquered, but he was overcome by his enemies and God. Alexander the Great thought he was the most powerful man alive before his defeat. Is pride a problem among us? What do passages such as Proverbs 6:16,17, Proverbs 15:25, and 1 Peter 5:5 mean to us? What makes a person proud? All of us have a need to be recognized and have confidence. How do we overcome the proud heart? How can we teach children to be humble? Is this a problem in our society? What contributes to this problem?

CHALLENGE FOR THE WEEK

Try to leave the word "proud" out of your vocabulary this week. Choose to say "thankful" or "grateful" instead.

SPECIAL CHALLENGES

1. Review, review, review.
2. Complete the research assignment.
3. Read a book on the Greek or Roman empire and report on it to the class.
4. Do some research on Alexander the Great.
5. Role-play the different religious groups incorporating their beliefs into the role-playing.
6. Do some research about the roads the Romans built. Draw a map showing the roads.

SUGGESTIONS FOR TEACHING

Sharing: We are studying about the dominion of the Greeks and Romans. Tell about someone in authority that you feel is doing a good job (government, school, or church leader.)

Prayer:

Options: 1.   Review previous history.
2.   Review and discuss the facts from the fact sheet.
3.   Provide research materials and allow the class to do research on the different groups and people.

Back to the Basics

4000 years in thirteen weeks
Or was it twenty-six?
People came from different groups
The class was quite a mix.

A teaching style we found real quick
Was not for naps or yawns
To keep up with it all, it seemed
Meant studying from the dawn.

We learned the motions to help us keep
A knowledge of the flow
We "framed," we "died," we mimicked
We put on quite a show.

We took tests when minds were dull
And learned from each new quiz.
We may not have had a bragging grade
But we tried to be a whiz!

We learned how sand mules and Jell-O
Could help us to recall
Bible books and events
That would stay with us all.

Our comfort zone was rattled
Our chairs we had to change
We learned plagues and commandments
And their order did arrange.

(continued)

Inspiration was the key
That was provided each.
We woke up and shook our brains
And spoke of goals to reach.

As in all settings there are some
Who shined and reached the peak
But us others glow with the knowledge
That there's hope for all who seek.

We are grateful for having
The will to work and share
And show through our actions
That we each should be aware.

Of gifts we have, both big and small
And how lucky we have been
So let's continue to meet new challenges
And not be sitters again!

—Faye Gibson

Chapter Thirteen

Review

REVIEW

Many facts and lessons can be learned from the Old Testament. It is easier to learn facts from activities and games. Learn to tell the story of the Old Testament in chronological order. Work with a friend to become an astute Bible student. Have fun while learning. Review! Review! Review!

SHARING

Share one lesson you have learned from this study.

The questions and review can be done outside class or in class. Role playing can be effective to reinforce the lesson.

Suggested games and teaching techniques are:

1. Tic-Tac-Toe (Divide into teams and each team gets an "X" or "O" when they answer a question correctly.)

2. Tic-Tac-Truth (Make a board of nine squares with nine different categories. Categories are: Spelling, Bible characters, Old Testament stories, New Testament stories, Who's speaking, Quotations, Miscellaneous, Bible Geography, and Special Occasions. Write questions in each category and play like tic-tac-toe. (Make the board so categories can be moved around.)
3. Divide the class into teams and role-play key stories.
4. Divide into groups of two and let each group work together on writing the answers to the review.
5. Divide into two teams and let each team answer a question and score a point.
6. Prepare a test using the review questions provided.

STUDY QUESTIONS

Summarize the following:

1. Genesis
2. Exodus
3. Leviticus
4. Numbers
5. Deuteronomy
6. Joshua
7. Judges
8. Ruth
9. 1 Samuel
10. 2 Samuel
11. 1 Kings 1–11
12. Judah
13. Israel
14. Babylonian Captivity
15. The Return
16. Between the Testaments

Name an event with which the book begins and ends

Genesis: Begins

               Ends

Exodus: Begins

               Ends

Numbers: Begins

               Ends

Joshua: Begins

               Ends

How many years does each cover?

Genesis   _____
Exodus   _____
Numbers   _____
Joshua   _____
Judges   _____
United Kingdom   _____
Israel   _____
Judah   _____
Babylon Captivity   _____
Between the Testaments _____

Can you?

1. Name the events on the days of creation. (Genesis 1, 2)
2. Name the 10 plagues. (Exodus 7–11)
3. Name the 10 Commandments. (Exodus 20, Deuteronomy 5)
4. Name the 15 judges. (Judges)
5. Name the kings of Israel. (1 Kings, 2 Kings)
6. Name the kings of Judah. (2 Chronicles)
7. Name the prophets to Israel.
8. Name the prophets to Judah.
9. Name the prophets during the Babylonian captivity.
10. Name the prophets after the return.

Identify the following places on a map

Garden of Eden	Mt. Sinai
Mt. Ararat	Kadesh-Barnea
Haran	Moab
Ur	Mt. Nebo
Canaan	Jericho
Egypt	Shiloh
Hebron	Philistines
Bethel	Jerusalem
Bethlehem	Tribe of Judah
Goshen	Babylon
Marah	Assyria
Rephidim	Persia

Identify the following characters:

Adam	Moses	Solomon
Cain	Amram	Ruth
Abel	Jochebed	Boaz
Noah	Miriam	Naomi
Shem	Aaron	Obed
Abraham	Jethro	Jonathan
Sarah	Zipporah	Goliath
Isaac	Eleazar	Bathsheba
Rebekah	Nadab	Queen of Sheba
Jacob	Abihu	Jeroboam
Rachel	Joshua	Rehoboam
Leah	Caleb	Ahab
Esau	Korah	Jezebel
Hagar	Baalam	Jonah
Ishmael	Balak	Hosea
Lot	Joshua	Amos
Judah	Rahab	Elijah
Joseph	Achan	Elisha
Benjamin	Deborah	Hezekiah
Pharaoh	Gideon	Josiah
Enoch	Samson	Athaliah
Terah	Samuel	Isaiah
Dinah	Saul	Jeremiah
Ephraim	David	King Nebuchadnezzar
Manasseh		King Cyrus
		Ezra
		Nehemiah
		Zerubbabel

HAVE FUN WHILE LEARNING BIBLE FACTS. SEE HOW MANY LESSONS YOU CAN PUT IN YOUR LIFE FROM THE STUDY OF THE OLD TESTAMENT.

Answers to the Short Answer Questions

Chapter 1: beginning; 2500 years; 50 chapters; Moses; creation; living in Egypt with everything going well; Adam, Noah, Abraham, Isaac, Jacob, Joseph; Noah; Shem, Ham, Japheth; Abraham, Rebekah; Jacob; Rachel; Ishmael and Isaac; Terah.

Chapter 2: exit; 400 years; the going out of Egypt; Egypt; Mt. Sinai; serpent becomes a snake, hand becomes leprous, water turns to blood; Amram, Jochebed; Gershom, Eliezar; Zipporah; Aaron and Miriam; Jethro or Reuel; Eleazar, Ithamar, Nadab, and Abihu; water to blood, frogs, lice, flies, disease of cattle, boils, hail, locusts, darkness, and death of the firstborn; there shall be no other gods before me, thou shall not bow down to a graven image, thou shall not take the name of the Lord in vain, remember the Sabbath to keep it holy, honor thy father and mother, thou shall not kill, commit adultery, steal, bear false witness or lie, and shall not covet.

Chapter 3: he married an Ethiopian; Miriam; Joshua, Caleb; earthquake; almonds; Balaam; Balak; Mt. Hor; that it was a good land, but giants were living there; they did not trust God and did not believe they could take the land.

Chapter 4: Exodus 20 and Deuteronomy 5; Nun; Rahab, that they would save her and her family; when they marched around God caused them to fall; silver, gold; a garment; of Achan's sin; dressed in old clothes and fooled Joshua making him think they were from a country far away; he commanded the sun to stand still; so a person could go and not be harmed when he/she killed someone accidentally; he cast lots.

Chapter 5: Jephthah; Gideon; Ehud; Samson; Joshua; Deborah; Achan; Samson; Gideon; Sisera; Shamgar; Samson; Rahab; Jael; Eglon; Samson; Naomi; Obed; Boaz; Elimelech.

Chapter 6: Agag; Abner; he offered the sacrifice and he didn't destroy all the Amalekites as God commanded; witch of Endor; Samuel; 40; Kish, to be like the nations around them; Abigail; Hannah and Elkanah; Michal, Jonathan, Eli; The Philistines.

Chapter 7: 120; Saul, David, and Solomon; 40; Jesse; Bathsheba; Absalom; Mephibosheth; Joab; Uzzah; 700 wives and 300 concubines; his wives and their gods; baby would die and the sword would not depart from his family; Joab; Bathsheba, Abigail, Ahinoam, Michal; 5; Amnon; Uriah; understanding heart; 7; "The half was not told me."

Chapter 8: Saul, David, and Solomon; making and worshiping idols; Rehoboam; 10; Jeroboam; Dan and Bethel; 250; 19; Assyrians; Elijah and Elisha; Jonah, Hosea, and Amos; Ahab, Jezebel; Naboth's; Naaman; Elisha; Elijah and the prophets of Baal; she and her husband built him a room and she was given a son, Elijah raised her son when he died.

Chapter 9: 1 Kings, 2 Kings, 2 Chronicles; Judah and Benjamin; Isaiah; Jeremiah; David; 350; Asa, Jehoshaphat, Hezekiah, Josiah;

young men; Ahab; Jehoram, Athaliah; God; she counseled her sons to do wickedly and she killed her family; 15, sundial; cleaned out the temple and declared a revival, Nebuchadnezzar.

Chapter 10: Nebuchadnezzar, Shadrach, Meshach, and Abednego, and Daniel; vessels; Daniel and Ezekiel; Belshazzar; Mene, Mene, Tekel, Upharsin; God has numbered your kingdom and has finished it or your kingdom will betaken away from you; Medes and Persians; Babylonian.

Chapter 11: Ezra and Nehemiah; Cyrus, Persia; Zerubbabel, Ezra, and Nehemiah; temple and the walls; Haggai, Zachariah, and Malachi; Sanballat, Tobiah, and Geshem.

Chapter 12: no questions.

Chapter 13: Look back in the previous chapters for the answers.

FOR REVIEW

TAKE A

Journey
Through
the
Old Testament

Genesis

Begins with (event) _____

Ends with (event) _____

Main Characters: _____

                              _____

                              _____

                              _____

                              _____

                              _____

                              _____

Lesson to Remember: _____

                        Years _____

Exodus

Begins with (event) _____

Ends with (event) _____

Main Character: _____

The **Ten Commandments** are recorded _____

Lesson to Remember: _____

                        Years _____

Leviticus

Tells about _____

Chapter 10 records the story of _____

Numbers

Begins with (event) _____

Ends with (event) _____

Story of _____

God decided they would not be able to go into the promised land when they were at _____ because
_____.

Called Numbers because _____

Lesson to Remember: _____

Deuteronomy

This book is a speech _____

Ten Commandments recorded in _____

The last chapter records _____ on _____

Lesson to Remember: _____

Joshua

The story of _____

They crossed _____ on _____.

They first took _____.

They failed at _____ because of the sins of
_____.

They took the land and divided it among the _____ tribes. The
Levites had _____ cities.

Main Character: _____

Lesson to Remember: _____

Years _____

Judges

Purpose of the judge _____

1.	Othniel	9.	Jephthah
2.	Ehud	10.	Ibzan
3.	Shamgar	11.	Elon
4.	Deborah	12.	Abdon
5.	Gideon	13.	Samson
6.	Abimelech	14.	Eli*
7.	Tola	15.	Samuel*
8.	Jair		

* We read of Eli and Samuel in 1 Samuel.

Lesson to Remember: _____

Years _____

Ruth

Story about _____

Took place during the time of the _____

Husband _____ Mother-in-law _____

Relationship to David _____

1 Samuel

Last two judges: _____ and _____

First king: _____ Ruled _____ years

Committed two great wrongs:

(1) Chapter 13: _____

(2) Chapter 15: _____

Lesson to Remember: _____

2 Samuel

Story of _____

"A man _____."

Sinned with _____

When Nathan told him of his sin, he replied, "_____."

Punishment: (1)_____

(2)_____

His son, _____, tried to take the kingdom away from him.

Lesson to Remember: _____

1 Kings 1–11

Story of _____

He was _____ and _____.

He asked God for _____.

He turned away from God and _____

Wives (how many) _____ Built _____

Concubines (how many) _____

Lesson to Remember: _____

Israel

We read of Israel in the books of _____,
_____, and _____.

Kings

1. Jeroboam	8. Ahaziah	15. Shallum
2. Nadab	9. Jehoram	16. Menahem
3. Baasha	10. Jehu	17. Pekahiah
4. Elah	11. Jehoahaz	18. Pekah
5. Zimri	12. Joash	19. Hoshea
6. Omri	13. Jeroboam II	
7. Ahab	14. Zachariah	

Tribes (10)

Prophets

1. _____
2. _____
3. _____

Two idols were placed at _____ and _____.

They were taken into captivity by the _____.

Lesson to Remember: _____

Years _____

Judah

We read of Judah in the books of _____,
_____, and _____.

Kings

1. Rehoboam
2. Abijam
3. Asa
4. Jehoshaphat
5. Jehoram
6. Ahaziah
7. Athaliah*

8. Joash (Jehoash)
9. Amaziah
10. Uzziah
11. Jotham
12. Ahaz
13. Hezekiah
14. Manasseh

15. Amon
16. Josiah
17. Jehoahaz
18. Jehoiakim
19. Jehoiachin
20. Zedekiah

*Queen

Tribes (2)

Prophets

1. Isaiah
2. Micah
3. Joel
4. Nahum

5. Habakkuk
6. Zephaniah
7. Jeremiah
8. Obadiah

They were taken into captivity by King _____,
king of the country of _____.

Lesson to Remember: _____

Years _____

Babylonian Captivity

We read this account in the book of _____.

Image in Dream
Daniel 2

Two prophets:
1. _____
2. _____

Meaning:

_____
_____
_____

_____
_____
_____
_____

The Babylonians were taken captive by the _____.

The book of _____ was written during the _____ captivity.

Lesson to Remember: _____

Years _____

Return to Judah

We read this story in the books of _____
and _____. King _____, king of
_____, freed the Jews and allowed them to return
to their land. Three men led a group back: _____,
_____, and _____.

They rebuilt the _____ and _____.

Three prophets after the return:

_____

_____

_____

Lesson to Remember: _____

Between the Testaments

Several things took place:

1. _____
2. _____
3. _____
4. _____
5. _____

Years _____

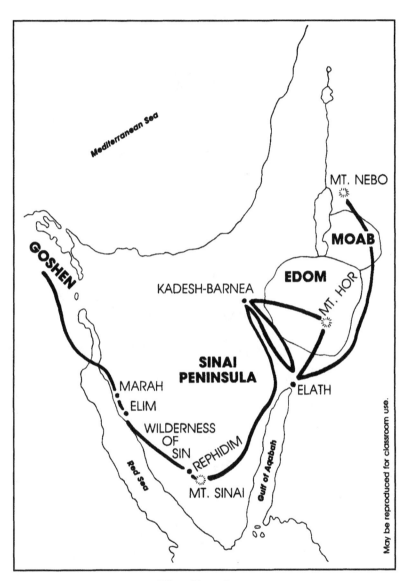

The Exodus

Dividing the Land Among the Tribes

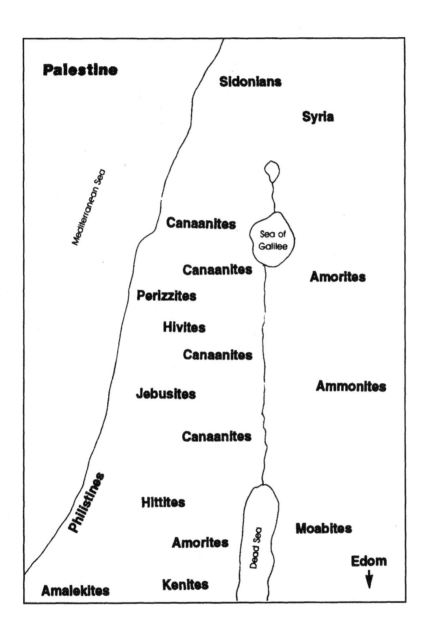

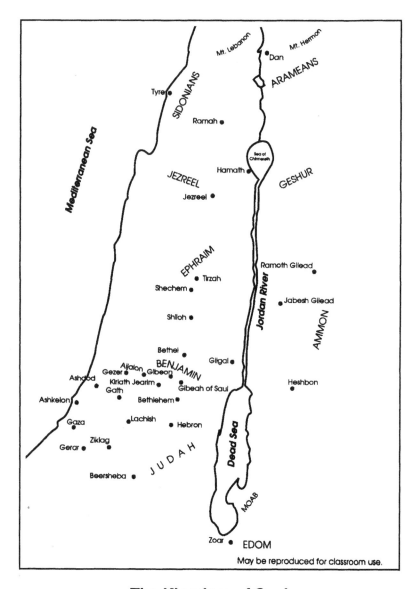

May be reproduced for classroom use.

The Kingdom of Saul

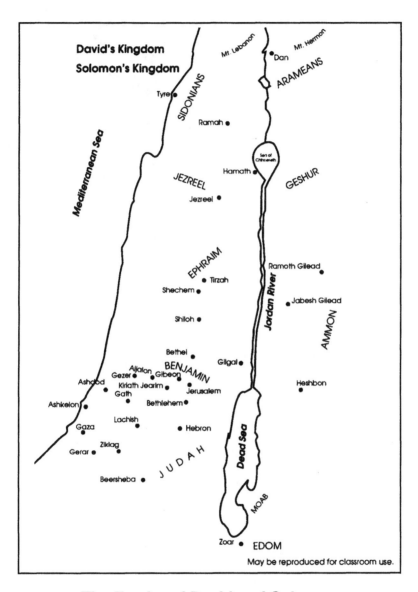

The Empire of David and Solomon

David's Kingdom
Solomon's Kingdom

Mt. Lebanon
Mt. Hermon
Dan
ARAMEANS
Tyre
SIDONIANS
Ramah
Sea of Chinnereth
Hamath
GESHUR
JEZREEL
Jezreel
Mediterranean Sea
EPHRAIM
Ramoth Gilead
Tirzah
Shechem
Jabesh Gilead
Jordan River
Shiloh
AMMON
Bethel
Gilgal
Ajalon BENJAMIN
Gezer Gibeon
Ashdod
Kiriath Jearim
Heshbon
Gath Jerusalem
Ashkelon
Bethlehem
Lachish
Gaza Hebron
Ziklag
Gerar JUDAH
Dead Sea
Beersheba
MOAB
Zoar EDOM

May be reproduced for classroom use.

The Kingdoms of Israel and Judah

1154   1075
1074   2772.21
  1166

CPSIA information can be obtained
at www.ICGtesting.com
Printed in the USA
JSHW041539220920
8135JS00002B/3